THE SECOND HALF

JOHN CRACE

THE SECOND HALF

THOUGHTS FROM A MALE MID-LIFE CRISIS

VISTA

First Published in Great Britain 1998
as a Vista paperback original

Vista is an imprint of the Cassell Group
Wellington House, 125 Strand, London WC2R 0BB

A catalogue record for this book is available from the British
Library

ISBN 0 575 60263 5

Designed and typeset
by Fishtail Design

Printed and bound in Great Britain by
Cox & Wyman Ltd, Reading, Berkshire

98 99   10 9 8 7 6 5 4 3 2 1

Disclaimer

I've been asked to point out that any similarity to any person living or dead is entirely the product of my mental instability. PROBABLY.

John Crace
June 1998

ONE

'Are you awake?'

'No.'

'How many more times are you going to make that pathetic little joke?' I said.

'How many more times are you going to ask me if I'm awake?' growled my wife.

Night-times weren't what they used to be. Long gone were the nights when we had a kiss and a cuddle and then settled down to eight hours' uninterrupted kip. The new regime went more like: crash out exhausted, wake up with a surge of adrenalin at 2.30 a.m. and then lie in bed worrying till 6.30, when the kids start their daily rampage. At least that was my regime. My wife selfishly still maintained the old one.

There's nothing worse than lying awake beside a sleeping partner. Especially if you have to do it day after day and week after week. Every contented snore, every languid rearrangement over the other side of the bed, is just another version of 'Fuck off, loser.' And frankly I'd have thought that she'd had more than enough of telling me how together she is and how neurotic I am during the daytime, without feeling the need to carry on in her sleep.

I can't remember the exact date my insomnia started. Nor have I any idea why. All I know is that it began with a vague feeling that things weren't right. That I hadn't done something that I was supposed to and that there wasn't a cat in hell's chance of rectifying it or achieving anything worthwhile the next day. Or ever, probably.

Now, though, I had become much more focused. I knew what I was worrying about. I was worrying about not sleeping. I lay awake, watching the luminous digital clock, and saw my life slipping away, willing myself, forcing myself to close my eyes and go to sleep. Without a great deal of success.

Initially I tried to be very considerate about my condition. I used to think that I mustn't rustle or fidget too much, in case I disturbed my wife. But I soon realized that such thoughtful behaviour went completely unacknowledged. She would wake up and show no signs of gratitude for my forbearance. And as it's pretty lonely being awake in the dark for hours on end, it seemed reasonable to expect her to share my predicament.

Though I didn't necessarily expect her to agree. On the rare occasions when she has woken up in the middle of the night of her own accord, she's been terrifyingly grumpy. So I had no intention of giving her a good shake and shouting, 'Hi. It's a great night. Let's have a chat.' A few surreptitious nudges didn't seem to make any difference either. Too much alcohol, I guess.

The only way to get her to wake up without attaching any blame to myself was to sneak into one of the kids' rooms, wake them up, make them cry and then tiptoe back to bed. I could keep her awake thereafter by incessantly asking her if she was awake.

'It's amazing how you wake up the moment Jo or Tom starts crying,' I said one morning.

'I'm an extremely intuitive mother, I suppose.'

'That's not quite what I was driving at.'

'So you're saying I'm a crap mother for waking up then,' she intuited.

Mums and guilt. A never-ending source of entertainment.

'No. I'm saying the kids clearly mean a great deal more to you than I do.'

'So?'

Shameless.

'Well, how do you think that makes me feel?' I said.

'Look. I need every moment's respite I can get from you. Eight hours is barely enough as it is, and if you think I'm going to listen to you drone on about your dreary

9

insomnia in the middle of the night, when you could easily nip downstairs and read a book, then you've another think coming.'

Which only went to show how self-centred she was. Because anyone with the slightest understanding of sleeplessness would know that you can't just go off and read a book. When you're worrying, you can't concentrate on anything but what you're worrying about. Distraction doesn't work. Anxiety demands your full attention.

Here's how a typical night's worrying would develop. It would start with the usual 'Oh shit, I'm awake again' drivel, which would then mutate into 'Do I need a piss?' This wasn't as straightforward as you might imagine, because the supplementary question 'How badly?' was impossible to judge. Because if I was to get back to sleep in the next ten minutes I could probably manage without going to the lav, but if I was going to be awake for an hour or so, then I would need to go. It was a hell of a conundrum, because I always wanted to believe that somehow this night was going to be one where my life went back to normal, so I felt I ought not to give in to my bladder. Yet experience dictated that I should just get up and go.

Experience usually won, not least because I would get so wound up that I was soon on the verge of wetting the bed. There then began a trawl of more everyday worries, such as 'How many of my friends earn more than me?', 'Do I actually have any friends?' and 'Is there a point at which things become pointless?' In which case some things must either have a point and be pointless at the same time, or there are no points and everything is pointless.

All of which mindless nonsense was merely a prelude to the real McCoy. The stuff that made my heart race and my palms sweat. Exactly when was I going to die?

Now, of course it could be that I'm already dead and that this is just an academic question. I don't mean as I'm writing. I'm not about to get all alternative and reincarnated on you. But I might be dead as you read this. There's a long delay between delivering a manuscript and publication, and to be honest anything could happen in the year it takes this book to make it into the shops. Heart attack, murder, car accident? Some poor bastard is going to cop one of these three nasty exits in the twelve months, and there's no guarantee it won't be me. Or, for that matter, you. I am not alone in this; we're all in it together. And if I'm going bonkers, then you're coming with me.

So how does it feel to imagine you are reading a book by someone who is dead? Someone who rather hoped to be still alive? What I'm really asking is whether you give a toss one way or the other. Because it makes a hell of a difference to me. I'm terrified of dying. I hate the idea of not existing. Which is a bit odd, I admit, as I don't have any problems with not having existed before I was born. My world began in 1956. Anything that may or may not have happened before then is only of passing historical interest. But then maybe it isn't so odd, as no one really has problems with beginnings: it's always the endings nobody wants to deal with.

Sooner or later, though, my life will end. And the longer I live the more likely I am to die. Time to talk specifics. I am forty-one years old. Rather too many of my friends have snuffed it already and I feel as if I'm accelerating up the queue. Even if I get lucky I am more than halfway through my life, as a bloke's life expectancy is somewhere in the mid-seventies.

Which makes me half-dead. My wife always accuses me of being depressingly negative when I say this. But she's wrong. It's actually a statement of profound optimism. For if someone were to offer me the choice of dropping down dead the day after my eightieth birthday in exchange for the certainty of getting there, I would take it like a shot. In fact, I would take it as a mega result. I would willingly trade off the possibility of making it to 100 for thirty-nine more inglorious years. But, as it is, I might well be three-quarters dead, seven-eighths dead. Even nineteen-twentieths dead. You just never know.

For the sake of argument, though, let's assume I'm only half-dead. Please. Humour me on this. It makes me feel less anxious. Being half-dead puts a lot of things into perspective. There are still many games to play, but all of them are futile. Except one. It's called Postponing the Inevitable.

TWO

Life begins at forty.

Mmm, course it does. Silly me. My teens, twenties and thirties have been nothing but a complete waste of everyone's time. My own especially. It would obviously have been far better to have been cryogenically frozen at birth, and then unleashed on to the world in pristine form on my fortieth birthday. God, what a drag it was to be young. To be able to stay up all night and feel great the next day. To watch *TFI Friday* without sneering. To look at young girls without feeling like a dirty old man. To be able to bend over without getting backache. Right. It was all real hard work.

Like hell. The only thing I will say for being forty is that life doesn't end. Necessarily. You see, I realized I was past it a long time ago. When I was thirty-four in fact. We were sitting around the kitchen table looking at the photos from our recent holiday, when my wife gave out a sudden shriek.

'Christ. Look at this,' she said. 'It's horrible.'

'What is it?' I asked.

'It's your head. You're going bald.' And she sniggered. Exactly why she found this piece of information quite so amusing was beyond me. I mean, if it was true it was her who was out and about with, and waking up next to, an ugly, old has-been. But she was quite obviously delighted, and it was her smirk which made me realize that she wasn't just winding me up.

Even so, I didn't want to believe it. I just didn't feel like a bald bloke. And as far as I knew, I hadn't been a bald bloke when I'd looked in the mirror that morning. In any case, it never pays to let my wife get away with anything.

'Oh, bollocks,' I said, with as much nonchalance as I could muster. 'Here, let me have a look.'

It wasn't good news. My wife had gone to some lengths to take the most unflattering picture of me she could manage. She had wedged herself halfway up a cliff face in the pouring rain so that she could get a shot of the top of my head, with my hair plastered down over my scalp. But there, unmistakably, was the outline of a small tonsure.

'What? You call that bald?' I said. 'Don't be fucking ridiculous. Anyone would look a bit thin on top from that angle and in that weather.' I'm not sure whether I sounded as unconvincing as I felt, but I have a nasty feeling that I did.

'Oh, come on, it's not that bad; it's only a small patch,' she replied, using the softly, softly approach before going in for the kill. 'Anyway, I'll still love you even if you don't have any hair.'

Didn't sound that likely to me.

Now, I dare say that some blokes are just able to shrug off going bald with the same ease that their heads shrug off their hair. 'Hey, it's just a normal bodily function,' they growl manlily. 'Besides, loads of women find baldness sexy,' they continue, falling for that other obvious patent untruth – along with the size of your dick not mattering – that men have propagated to make themselves feel better. It seems fairly straightforward to me. A woman would much rather have a bloke with his own hair and a decent-sized knob, than a balding saddo with a micro-dick. I mean, uncontroversial, or what?

Whichever way I looked at it, the outlook was piss-poor. There was no way my hair was going to miraculously re-sprout – unless I took the Elton John option, and that was even more pathetic than going bald. All I had to look forward to was a slow – or possibly rapid – descent into slaphead status. And I couldn't think of a single redeeming feature. I even tried imagining what it must be like to be Nick Hornby. Loads of people reckon that writing is his major talent. After all, the man has invented a new literary genre, has sold screenplays and made a few mill in the process. Now, I don't want to knock this – I'm a fan, but it does seem to rather miss the point. You see, he's managed to do all this while being completely bald. *That* is what's remarkable. Moreover, his lack of growth really doesn't seem to bother him: whenever you see his pic somewhere he always looks positively jolly. I don't know how he does it. Perhaps he's got a most ginormous cock.

'Are you OK?' said my wife, putting on her best faux-caring voice, but still unable to conceal her smirk.

Lapsing into a depressed dreamworld was getting me nowhere. It was time to do something. I reached over for the photos and started to flick through them. Eventually I found one that I thought would do.

'This is a nice one of you,' I said, having picked out the least attractive one I could find.

'Pass it over,' said my wife, clearly surprised that I could take any interest in a photo that didn't have me in it. Her face instantly collapsed into a deep frown. 'I don't think it's that good. In fact, I think I look like shit.'

'God. You're so vain. Here, let me have another shufti.' I pretended to scan it intently for ten seconds or so. 'Yeah, perhaps you're right. Maybe you're not looking your best. You do seem a bit porkier than usual, but that's probably just a trick of the light.'

'You're saying I'm fat,' she snapped.

'Calm down. I'm not saying anything of the sort.' But I'm glad you think so, I thought.

'You are. You're saying I'm fat.'

'I'M NOT,' I said, registering a shout that I hoped

would be taken for a sign of deep hurt that my honest intentions had been so badly misrepresented.

'You are,' she sulked, somewhat appeased.

'Just forget it. In any case, I still love you.'

YES. YES. YES. That'll teach her to fuck with me. With honour satisfied, I decided to let the matter rest. I gave her a smoochy kiss and we settled down to a romantic evening in front of the TV. But while it was quite nice to come away with a draw after a strong second-half performance in that particular little skirmish, I was more than a little aware that I had a major problem. You can gain weight and you can lose it. Hair you can only lose.

Obviously, it's easy to keep tabs on your hair if you're going bald from the front. You just look in the mirror and watch as your forehead gets bigger and bigger. But keeping an eye on what's happening on the dark side is practically impossible. And that's why I was so shocked by my predicament. It felt as if my body had been playing tricks on me behind my back. There I'd been, swaggering down the street, giving off the confident, cool vibes of the fully haired, when everyone who was walking behind me was thinking, What a tosser. Doesn't he realize he's going bald?

My immediate priority was to assess the damage. Which was far easier said than done, because it was extremely hard to get a rear aerial view. I barricaded myself into the bathroom, rigged up a complicated series of mirrors covering all four walls, and with some complicated physical manoeuvring – phew, I wasn't completely over the hill, thank God – managed to locate the danger zone. And it was undeniably there. It wasn't quite in the Bobby Charlton league – there was a smattering of tufts still partially covering the crown – but quite clearly a significant number of follicles had gone AWOL.

At this point, I have to say, I burst into tears. Not hysterical tears, no violent sobs, but a gentle, plangent lament for the end of my youth. There was no two ways about it. I was inexorably turning into my dad.

Now, I've often been a sucker for any quick-fix solution in the past. Got a headache, do some smack, got a toothache, take some coke – that sort of thing. But somehow I knew that none of the so-called 'new, advanced trichological formulas' would make the slightest difference, other than make me considerably poorer. Besides which, I couldn't have stood the shame of having a bucketful of hair restorer lodged in the bathroom next to the shampoos.

The one measure I did take was to almost completely stop washing my hair. This might seem extreme, but I'd heard that hair started cleaning itself after three months, and twelve weeks of a lanky, greasy rug seemed a small price to pay for the torture of hair washing. You see, after every wash I would find stray hairs floating in the bath, and while I couldn't be sure they weren't errant pubes, I was pretty sure they were coming out of my head. And so every time I let the water out it felt as if my life was going down the plug-hole. Literally.

Besides which, bath water can lead you into a false sense of security. Sometimes when I dared to bathe there would be no furry residue left around the side of the tub. And when this happened twice in a row I concluded that my baldness had self-arrested. God, I felt good that day. So hunky . . . so young. I dashed out of the bathroom and celebrated with twenty one-arm press-ups and some old Julie Burchill columns.

But the return to yoofdom was short-lived. Because when I got round to being scientific about it, my hair was still on the way out. I had this old pair of dividers – you know, the things that you never needed that came with the compass, the pencil and the ruler in the old Helix maths accessory tins – which turned out to be just the job for measuring the decline in vegetation. I simply stuck one point into one edge of the bald patch and stretched the dividers out until I could ram the other point into the far side. As you can imagine, this was often a rather painful process, but it was both necessary in terms of accuracy – especially when you're measuring to the nearest millimetre – and also quite therapeutic. I needed to let my head know how angry I was about what it was up to.

There was no escaping the fact that my hair was still on the way out. Which was weird, because if it wasn't going down the plug-hole then where the hell was it going? It took one of my random all-over body checks for moles, lumps and tumours to enlighten me. Areas of my body that had hitherto been covered just by skin were now entrapped under a downy matting. I'd never had a completely hairless torso – I think it looks a bit naff, like you're too wet to grow any – but I had been quite pleased with the previous arrangement. A few tufts delicately positioned between my pecs to proclaim my sexuality, but nothing too aesthetically displeasing. But now, areas of my stomach, and worse still, my shoulders, back, ears and nose, had turned into an allotment.

I was still a long way off turning into a gorilla, mind. My face and chest hadn't joined up into a fitted carpet and I didn't have the worrying decision of where to stop shaving each day. 'Sir is wearing a T-shirt today. I suggest sir lowers the Plimsoll line a little.' But the signs weren't promising; clearly my hair was going to move from my head to invade my body. Scientists call it the Law of Conservation of Matter; I call it a fucking outrage. Women don't know how lucky they are sometimes.

It seems to work in different ways for different blokes. For some, their hair recedes dramatically at the front, only to elongate itself at the back into a pony-tail. Which, on balance, would have been a great deal worse than what I was lumbered with. Even so, turning into a lollipop on a Simian stick was hardly something to look forward to.

Of course, all hair inspections had to be done in private and all worries kept to myself. You can't talk to other blokes about it because blokes are supposed to be in control of this sort of thing. If your hair's falling out it's because you're letting it. Right? Right. And as for my wife.

Well, you can forget her. Compassion has never been one of her strong points.

'What is it, now?' she asked, dragging herself away from her fascinating Jackie Collins. She'd like you to think she's up to her neck in Margaret Forster or some such. But she isn't. Trust me. You're going to get to know her quite well and it's best I don't let her pull the wool over your eyes.

'Umm, er, nothing much,' I replied, unwilling to submit myself to another of her merciless, scabrous attacks.

'It's your hair again,' she continued, putting the boot in regardless.

'As a matter of fact, it is,' I said, trying to be all new-mannish and upfront with my anxieties.

'Christ, you are just so bloody pathetic,' she screamed. 'You've lost a few hairs at the back of your head and you're acting as if it's the end of the sodding world.'

And they say that it's men who have difficulty relating to women.

'You don't really understand, do you?' I said, trying to be reasonable.

Sometimes it helps to state the obvious. Not on this occasion, though.

'It's you that doesn't understand, you berk. You've still got nearly all your hair. You haven't even really got a bald patch. You're thinning ever so slightly at the back and since you're quite tall no one even notices it except when you insist on pointing it out.'

'OK, OK, calm down. So what you're saying is that as long as I never sit down, have every building taller than a bungalow razed to the ground and abolish double-decker buses, then no one will notice my head?'

'Oh, do belt up.'

'Fine. Have it your way, then. I'd just like to say that provided you never go out no one will notice the lines on your face.'

'Aaaaaagh.'

So, you can see why I've had difficulty broaching the subject of the grey bits that have recently emerged near my temples.

THREE

Sorry. I didn't mean to come back to hair quite so soon. But I'm not sure if I've made myself perfectly clear. I've got no attachment to hair *per se*. I feel no angst about brutalizing my stubble with a blunt razor. Because I know that however badly I treat it, it's going to come back for more.

But when your head hair drops out, that's it. Finito. I guess that if all blokes were dome-heads, then I wouldn't really miss it, but that's beside the point. What gets me is that hair loss is so random, so unfair. Some men get to eighty with a full thatch, while others start losing it in their twenties. I suppose I should be grateful that my hair managed to hold on for ten years longer than the bare minimum, but I'm not. How could I be when I still get the odd spot? Going from puberty straight to senility is too much for anyone to take.

Your body has all sorts of ways of letting you know you're getting older, but none is more obvious than going bald. If there's any women out there who think I'm making a bit of a fuss about nothing, then just think about this. How would you like it if it was happening to you? How would you like to have your decay, your mortality, shoved in your face every minute of every day? Believe me, it's not nice. It affects the way you think, the way you feel and the way you behave. Do you think Peter Stringfellow would carry on the way he does if his hair was falling out? Of course not. But clearly he still wakes up every morning, looks in the mirror and sees David Ginola. What's even more amazing is that there appears to be a never-ending stream of women who also see David Ginola.

Put simply, going bald is life's way of letting you know you're fucked. A short while ago loads of people were getting terribly worked up about Martin Amis spending 20K on having his teeth fixed, condemning him for being shallow and vain. But the operation had nothing to do with ending up with gleaming white, straight gnashers to help him pull; it was all about the titanium and tungsten rod implants. There's nothing wrong with my teeth – yet – but if I had 20K to spare I'd have the implants too. Because they'll last for ever. Long after Marty has decomposed six feet under, long after *Money* and *London Fields* have gone out of print, long after his last relative has forgotten all about him, there will be a part of him that remains. A tangible legacy, if you like. And cheap at the price.

Losing your hair makes you neurotic. And if you meet a bloke who claims he doesn't get neurotic, then he's either a liar or lobotomized. The main manifestation of my neurosis was an overwhelming compulsion to count things. Like most psychoses, it started off as an innocent distraction. I was lying in bed, anxiously awake, at some God-forsaken time of the morning.

'Seven thousand four hundred and seventy-eight. Seven thousand four hundred and seventy-nine.'

'What the hell are you droning on about?' groaned my wife drowsily.

'I'm counting,' I replied. I would have thought that she might have been able to work that out for herself, but with my wife you can't take anything for granted.

'I know that,' she hissed.

So why bother to ask then?

'I meant,' she went on, 'what are you counting?'

'You don't really want to know.'

'Since you've woken me up, you might as well tell me, though.'

'I didn't wake you up. You woke up. There's a difference. Waking you up implies an inten—'

'Don't be so fucking irritating. What were you counting?'

'The number of lovers I've had.' I wish.

'Oh. Ha, ha.'

I was beginning to enjoy this. It's very lonely being awake all by yourself in the middle of the night and having no one to annoy. But the main reason I didn't want to tell her the truth was that it was so sad. I was actually counting the number of hairs I had probably already lost. I'd made a rough calculation of how many hairs a bloke can expect to have per square inch and I was trying to work out what percentage might remain. From this I figured I would be in with a shout of calculating at what point my baldness would be obvious from the front, and when I would have so little hair that I would have to do the butch thing and give my remaining pride and joy a number-two cut to make it look as if I was so hard I didn't give a toss.

'I was counting fish, if you really want to know,' I said feebly.

'Fish?'

'Yeah, fish. It makes a change from sheep. When you spend as long awake as me, you get bored of counting the same things night after night.'

I don't think she believed me, but she was too tired to push it. Besides, on balance, she would prefer to think of me as being a bit weird rather than downright devious.

But I didn't get bored of counting hair. I became obsessed by it. In fact, sometimes I wondered whether it wasn't the anticipation of my nocturnal maths that kept waking me up the whole time.

Whatever. It wasn't long before my arithmamania intruded on my daytime thoughts as well. And the numbers that began to preoccupy me the most were those between one and eighty. Because when I began to think about it properly, there weren't actually very many.

4

When you're a kid, eighty seems very, very old. Unimaginably old. You don't think, Ooh I'm five now, so I've probably already had one-sixteenth of my life. You don't think, I've only got seventy-five birthdays and Christmases to go. When you're small it feels as if the rest of your life can accommodate an infinite number of birthdays and Christmases. An Action Man or Barbie fest from here to kingdom come.

But the law of diminishing returns starts operating when you get to forty. How can anyone enjoy a birthday or Christmas when it's just another notch on the way to death? Moreover, with one or two friends having already – albeit against their better judgement – decided to die, how could I be sure I was going to be around for any more annual festivities? And if I couldn't, I was buggered if I was going to make a big song and dance about Christmas. 'Oh goody, I'm going to die soon. Let's have a party to celebrate.'

The trouble is, you're expected to enjoy Christmas, especially when you've got children. They have this absurdly naive optimism that everything is just fab at Christmas, and it's considered very bad form to disabuse them. So for some years I went through a bizarre form of cognitive dissonance with my kids. I would follow an elaborate ritual of trying to wear a perma-smile, while just longing for the day to end. I knew the whole thing was absurd. I didn't get overly worked up about dying on days, such as 9 January, which logic told me I had just as few of as 25 Decembers. But somehow Christmas Day brought everything into focus.

I developed what I thought was a brilliant plan for coping with this. I would try to make out that Christmas wasn't really happening. I would – because I'm a giving sort of person – allow the kids a token present, but everything else was barred. We didn't have grandparents, aunts or friends over, and we always had a chicken for lunch rather than turkey. And it all worked reasonably well. I felt only moderately suicidal.

But for some reason I was unfairly characterized as a killjoy. Even my mother got in on the act. Never the most direct of people, she once sent me a revolting bright-red sweatshirt with a huge grinning Santa on the front. Which was her way of saying 'Get a Life', though what she actually said was, 'I thought you and the children might have a laugh at this.' Oh we did, we did. Especially when I binned it.

So, come late last November, I was half expecting some direct action from the wife. Sure enough.

'Are you going to ruin Christmas for us all again this year?'

She's all charm. With such an understanding attitude to other people's problems.

'If I possibly can.'

Two can play at that game.

'No, you're not,' she said. 'Because you're going to do something about it.'

'Like what? Take a fistful of mogadon on Christmas Eve? Fly Concorde over the international date-line?'

'No. You're going to get help.'

It wasn't going to involve her, then.

'Take a look at this,' she went on, handing me an item she had cut out from the paper. 'Relate are running a one-day workshop for Christmasphobes in two weeks' time. It sounds like just the sort of thing you could do with.'

Unusually, she was right. It sounded great, not least because, if it didn't work, then no one could accuse me of not having made an effort.

So I rang up Southampton City College, where the course was to take place, and got them to send me an application form. It arrived by return of post. I filled it in, wrote out a cheque for £35 and indelibly inked the second Saturday in December into my diary. This is it, I thought.

A bit of touchy-feely caring and sharing with a bunch of fellow-depressives and it will be 'Yo-ho-ho' and *Jingle Bells* from here on in. I felt so positive I splashed out on a couple of advent calendars for the kids. Which turned out to be a bit of a mistake. Because ten days later I got a phone call.

'Is that Mr Crace?'

'Er . . . yes,' I said cautiously. I still can't get used to the idea of anyone calling me 'Mr'. I always think it's my dad they're after.

'It's Southampton City College. I'm afraid we've got a bit of a problem with the Christmas workshop.'

'What sort of problem?'

'It's a bit embarrassing, really. We haven't got the numbers we anticipated. So we're going to have to cancel. But thanks very much for your interest, and we'll be returning your cheque.'

Great. Excuse me while I top myself. If it's not already sad enough being prepared to get up at 7 a.m. on a Saturday morning in December to rattle off the eighty miles to Southampton, it's just plain desperate to discover there is no one else in the rest of southern England who feels as bad about Christmas as you do.

A few days later, presumably as some kind of sop to my shattered self, an envelope containing the full info on what was supposed to have taken place on the course plopped through the letter-box with a heavy thud.

'That's handy,' I said.

'What is?' asked my wife.

'A group-therapy course with no group. "So, how do you feel about that, John?" "Pretty pissed off, John." '

'Don't be so negative. You might find something quite useful in there. Why don't you have a look at it this weekend? You haven't got anything better to do.'

Thanks for reminding me. My life is so empty and meaningless that spending an hour wading through a heap of psychobabble is something to look forward to.

I woke early that Saturday morning, feeling tense.

'What's the matter, Daddy?' said the kids, sensing my nervousness.

'I'm learning how to enjoy myself.'

The sweet thing is they thought I was joking.

I settled down in front of my desk and started leafing through the papers.

'Hello course,' I said.

'Hi, John,' one of them replied. 'Thank you for taking the time to look at us. I guess we ought to start by introducing ourselves. We are going to be your trainers. Now my name is Page One.'

'And I'm Page Two.'

'And I'm Page Three.'

After Page Twenty-eight had made herself known, Page Seven chipped in again:

'We ought to stress that confidentiality is absolutely paramount in this group.'

'Well, I won't tell anyone if you don't,' I replied.

Hey, this was easier than expected. I think I was making real progress.

'OK,' said Page Four. 'It's time to have a look at some Myths sheets. For instance, John, do you believe in Father Christmas?'

How old did she think I was, for fuck's sake? Could you imagine going along to a course and finding someone who believed in Santa Claus? What would you say? Get a grip, loser? Or I'm really sorry to have to let you know that Father Christmas doesn't exist? And what would they do? Burst into floods or say, 'Thank you for that. I now feel free to enjoy the rest of the holiday.'

'Er, no.'

'That's good, John, very good,' said Page Four earnestly. 'You're really tackling your Christmas issues head on.'

'Let's move on,' Page Nine butted in. 'What are your hopes and expectations of both Christmas and the course?'

I wrote down 'making it through to next year without going bonkers'. Page Nine looked over my shoulder. 'Time for coffee,' he sighed.

That was better. I was feeling much refreshed, even though I'd had to make it myself, while the twenty-eight Pages just stared at me in silence. I was ready for anything.

'What rules operate in your house?' asked Page Fourteen.

'Umm . . . I wasn't aware that we had any. Unless you count "We shall have a row".'

There was just one more item to go before lunch. Oh

God. It was 'Forcefield Analysis for Change', run by Page Nineteen. One of the Californian Pages, I presumed. Now what the fuck was all that about? Being the moron that I am, I didn't have a degree in quantum physics and I had missed the relevant episode of *Star Trek*.

'I think I'll pass on this one,' I said.

'I'm picking up a lot of hostility towards me, John,' said Page Nineteen.

Well spotted.

'Coping better,' said Page Twenty.

'Not really, but thanks for asking.'

'No. "Coping Better". It's the title of the first session after lunch.'

'Oh.'

My relationship with Page Twenty never recovered from that misunderstanding.

'Time for some assertiveness training,' shouted Pages Twenty-one, Twenty-two and Twenty-three in unison. 'We want you to be specific, clear and direct. Say what you feel without wrapping it up in hints.'

'I fucking hate Christmas,' I ventured. 'Is that specific, clear and direct enough?'

Page Twenty-five was a prize bully.

'My topic is "Working with Weapons",' she said.

'I thought I was here to natter my way out of trouble, not to resort to violence.'

'You don't get it,' she menaced. 'You just don't get it at all.'

'Maybe I'm just not pragmatic enough.'

Which just left the course evaluation.

'How did you find it?' they chorused.

'Brilliant.'

'Good. Now it's traditional to close by giving everyone a Christmas card.'

You know where you can shove your sodding Christmas cards.

'I don't think I've got any spare,' I said limply.

'How did you get on, then?' my wife asked nervously as I wandered downstairs.

'I'm a very happy bunny and I'm looking forward to Christmas enormously.'

'No, seriously.'

'Really seriously? I've come up with one good insight, I suppose.'

'And what's that?'

'Every Christmas I survive is one less to bother about in the future.'

FIVE

'Excuse me. Can you help me?'

There's worse things that can happen to you walking down Farringdon Road than being accosted by an attractive woman in her early twenties. So, I was more than ready to help. Carry her bags, buy her a drink – anything. Believe me.

'Yeah, sure,' I said, wondering what my hair was up to while trying to sound urbane, cool and ten years younger.

'Can you tell me where the tube station is, please?'

It wasn't my body she was after, then. Well, you can always hope.

'Er . . . Carry on down here for a hundred yards or so, turn left and you can't miss it,' I said, anxious to prove that I had a lively mind at least.

'That's great, thanks.'

Yeah, and thank you too. For nothing. Next time you're lost why don't you wander round in circles for half an hour instead of bothering me with your dreary little problems? Because while it's only directions to you, it's my life we're talking about. I know the reason you approached me. It wasn't that subconsciously you found me sexually irresistible. You came up to me because you thought I was safe. You didn't think, Gosh, he's good-looking, or He's quite cute, or even He's fuck ug, because you just don't think of blokes my age in those terms. Having sex with me is a conceptual impossibility. It would be like shagging your dad. Who – come to think of it – might well be younger than me anyway.

I don't want to be safe. I hate the idea of being safe. I want to be dangerous, menacing, elusive, enigmatic and devastatingly, drop-dead gorgeous. I want women to be nervous about talking to me in case their latent desires show through. Well, I can just dream on, because it's just not going to happen. I've had my sexual peak and it's downhill from here on in.

Which is just so . . . unfair. Because I never had what I would call a sexual peak. More of the odd ripple, really. When I was in my late teens most girls I knew wanted to go out with an older man. 'They're so much more mature, more interesting,' they would twitter to each other, which was their way of saying 'have more money'. But now that I have more money and have reached mythical older-man status all the women have mysteriously dematerialized. So either the girls were talking a whole load of bollocks or else fashions have changed.

But then, generally speaking, apart from a brief period in my twenties, I always seem to have been the wrong age. Even the girls who didn't want a much older man didn't want me. Now, you never expected a girl to go out with a bloke the same age or younger than you, because they just didn't do that sort of thing. It was beneath them. But you might have thought that I would have stood a chance with a sixteen-year-old when I was eighteen. But no. They all wanted a seventeen- or nineteen-year-old apparently. Perhaps it was just personal, after all.

Regret is a killer. But it's unavoidable when you get to forty. You look back on all those times when you could have, just maybe, you know, if you had bought that extra drink, rolled that last joint, hadn't been too mean to give her some of your coke and had put on that killer James Taylor track – personally, I always thought he was unbearably wet, but he was an incredibly big hit with women – then you might have got another bit of leg-over.

The trouble is, I never had any confidence. Your average girl always seemed to be so knowing, so aloof, that I was always pathetically grateful for any attention I got. And the ones that weren't knowing and aloof I didn't fancy. So I would spend hours hanging around hoping that some girl would take pity on me and invite me to shag her. Because I could never have asked her to shag me, in case she said no. It's just about tolerable to go without sex, but being turned down for being physically repulsive is too much.

Even the first snog I ever got happened by accident. I was standing at a party chatting to this girl, when I noticed her eyes glazing over. She then grabbed me, attached her lips to mine, forced my mouth open as I gasped for breath and stuck her tongue down the back of my throat. It's amazing where being a dull conversationalist can get you, but thanks anyway, Serena. And as for my first shag? Well, even I could get the message when Teresa said, 'It's all right. I am on the pill, you know.'

All this may just seem like everyday stuff – I hope so anyway. It's not just me, is it? Is it? But please bear with me, because I have a major confession that affects every one of you. My sexual inadequacy has changed the course of history. Let me explain.

It was a few days before our wedding, and my wife and I were finalizing our prenuptial agreement. A naff idea, I know, but it wasn't mine. Which makes it . . . Oh, let's not get into that. 'Blame' is such an ugly word.

'What do you think of fidelity?' she asked.

Could she really imagine I was stupid enough to fall for that one? As if I was going to admit I was finding the idea of never going to bed with another woman somewhat hard to come to terms with.

'I think fidelity is the absolute bedrock of a good, Christian marriage,' I replied.

'Oh, do belt up,' she said nicely. 'I'm actually finding it rather hard to come to terms with never sleeping with another man.'

I was sure that it was only blokes that thought like this. Things were looking distinctly unpromising. Maybe she was going to tell me she was a transsexual.

'I see.'

'Look, it's no big deal. Surely you must worry about never sleeping with another woman? Don't you?'

'Hadn't really given it much thought,' I lied. 'But now you mention it, I suppose I do.'

A brief silence ensued, in which we looked rather awkwardly at each other. I could tell she had some plan up her sleeve, but she was clearly too embarrassed to come out with it, so I decided to make her sweat a while.

'So what do you suggest we do about it, then?' I asked eventually.

'Well, I thought that we might each nominate some-one we could go to bed with who wouldn't really count as infidelity.'

It was better than I feared. I had assumed her notion of a fair arrangement would be for her to shag whoever she liked, and for me to shag no one. Which, come to think of it, is the sort of deal I would have come up with. Even so, it wasn't looking good. She had obviously been giving this a lot of thought and had someone definite in mind. Time to find out.

'Who do you want?'

'Daley Thompson,' she said promptly. 'What about you?'

My mind went blank.

'Come on. Make your mind up, dimwit,' she pressed. 'It can't be that difficult to think of someone.'

But it was. When you've only got one shot, you've got to get it right. But, like a moron, I let myself be hurried into blurting out the first name that came to mind.

'Princess Diana.'

And with that the prenuptial agreement was sealed. She could have Daley and I could have Di. And at the time I reckoned that she was far more likely to get lucky, especially as she devoted most of her summers to travelling to athletics meetings in Britain and mainland Europe. But it was me who came closest.

I had been invited to the opera – yes, I am that kind of guy. Culturally extremely sophisticated, though in a very understated kind of way, you understand – and I happened to look up at the Royal Box, and who should be there but Di. God, she looked gorgeous, and I just couldn't stop staring. And you know what? She looked down and held my gaze – not just for a second, but for a long time. And what her gaze said to me was, 'Help me, John. Unlock me from my loveless marriage. Make me whole.'

We've now got to the bit that I feel so bad about. Because I did nothing. Absolutely bugger all. I just sat rooted to the spot, watching her become ever more desperate at my inertia. And when she finally realized that I just didn't have the bottle – wasn't the man she had taken me for – she gave me a final look of utter sadness and looked away. I can't forgive myself for this. I feel responsible for her death. For had I allowed her – with my wife's blessing, naturally – to find happiness with us, then she might still be alive today. Instead of racing through Paris in a black Merc at 120mph, she could have been gridlocked in a pale-blue Vauxhall Astra Starmist (automatic) on Streatham High Road.

My wife was probably the only person in Britain who didn't find Princess Di's funeral unbearably moving. For her, it was the demise of a love rival, leaving her free to shag Daley senseless and me with no comeback. So now I'm stuck. I've tried asking if I could bring on a substitute – and I've thought of a number of likely candidates in the years since I was railroaded into making a swift decision – but my wife is utterly intransigent. Fidelity it is, then.

Not that there's anything wrong with fidelity. In fact, it's got a lot going for it. Like both partners growing old at the same rate. Monogamy is a bit like entering a time warp. When you're single you have to make a bit of an effort to pull. You have to know what's trendy and what's not. But once you've become a fully functioning unit, all that ends. You keep the same haircut, wear the same sort of clothes and listen to the same desperate music. And make no mistake, this is not laziness – it's necessity. Because keeping all the accessories from the time when you first met enables you to indulge in corporeal distortion. Beer gut? What beer gut? Droopy tits? What droopy tits? Hairline?

What hairline? A little imagination goes a long way in the shagging stakes.

Assuming that you've got an imagination, of course. Bizarrely, for someone as deluded as myself, I've never been able to pull the wool over my eyes when it comes to sex. As hard as I try, I just can't see myself as a love god. I guess it comes from not being able to keep a straight face when saying 'I'm hot for you babe.' (Or is it 'chick'? I must check.) Whatever. It's fucking inconvenient. Because it makes your average 'getting lucky is not a complete impossibility' night *chez* Crace go a bit like this.

Wife gets in late – long after I've put the kids to bed. Don't get me wrong. I'm not after the sympathy vote here. Normally, it's me who's back last – anything to get out of do-mestic responsibilities. But lurve nights usually begin with her getting in about nine, feeling raunchily independent.

She'll drone on about the kids for a bit.

'Did you get them off to bed OK?' she'll ask.

This always manages to irritate me. Must be why she does it. Does she think I'm a complete moron? Don't answer that – it was only rhetorical. Hasn't she heard of mind-bending drugs like Valium? Or Calpol for the kids?

'Yes.'

'Any problems?'

Same old story. She thinks I can't do the job. OK, you want problems, I'll give you problems.

'Yeah, Tom was a little bastard in the bath. I had to give him a right slapping.'

She can't bear the idea of anyone touching her toy boy.

'You slapped him?'

'Yeah. But I didn't mark him. The social worker will never know.'

'So you didn't slap him then?'

Not much gets past her.

Pretty romantic so far, huh? Just don't judge all foreplay by your own conventional standards. Anyway. Things can go in one of two directions at this point. A full-scale row or, just occasionally, my wife will let it drop. And after a few moments she might say, 'You look great tonight.'

A compliment from her is to be treated with maximum suspicion. It usually means she's pissed. She hates it if I start sniffing her breath, but I have to find out.

'How many fingers am I holding up?' I say, flashing my hand in front of her face.

'What?'

'H-O-W M-A-N-Y F-I-N-G-E-R-S A-M I H-O–'

'Oh, fuck off. I haven't been drinking. Why do you always assume I've had a drink if I get back late?'

Got me there. I'm completely stumped. It couldn't possibly be anything to do with the fact that she normally dives into the pub as soon as she can.

'I wasn't assuming anything. That's why I was checking.'

'What is your problem?'

Problems. It's always problems. And I'm so easygoing.

43

'Nothing. I was just surprised that you said I look great.'

'I was trying to be nice.'

This is getting confusing. Because if she's not pissed, there must be some ulterior motive. Perhaps she is having an affair.

'Why do you lie to me, if you're trying to be nice?' I ask.

'What are you talking about?'

'Well, clearly I'm not looking great. I haven't looked great for at least ten years. Added to which, I'm knackered and my hair is falling out.'

'OK, you're right. You're not looking great. You're just not looking terrible, that's all. Which is the best you can expect at your age.'

'So why did you try to humiliate me by saying I looked great?'

'Christ, you're dim. I was trying to be friendly. Maybe even seduce you.'

'Why don't you just give us a snog, rather than be so damned subtle?'

And with that she rips off her clothes and flings herself at me and we embark on a two-hour sex marathon. Obviously.

But what I want to know is, how can I be sure I'll get a repeat performance? When you're in your twenties this sort of thing just doesn't bother you. 'Cos you'll probably be getting it in a couple of hours or so and you're more likely worrying about how you can get out of it. But these days it's all a bit more critical. How do I know that I haven't just had the last stiffy I'm ever going to get? I may die tomorrow or my dick might just stop working. It happens. It's at moments like these that I wish I had a better relationship with my dad. Then I could ask him, 'Can you still do it?' and he could say, 'Yes' or 'No' and we could get down to the nitty-gritty of male sexuality. As it is, I'm far too embarrassed to ask him, so I have to carry on racked with doubt about when I'm likely to wind up impotent.

Which makes each shag of vital importance. You see, it would be all right to go out on a big high – when you both come simultaneously after trying out dozens of positions. But imagine if your last time was a premature ejaculation? Then your life wouldn't be worth living – you would know that your partner would for always remember you as the world's worst shag. And you'd carry the knowledge into your old age that your indoors was busy telling all the other OAPs about your shortcomings. Worse still, there's bound to be one old Jack Nicholson type from the Darby & Joan club who can still get a hard-on and he'll getting all the action in his sixties that you should have been getting in your twenties.

Women are lucky here. Even as they get older, they can still function sexually. I mean, there's not so much expected of them. And if things get a bit tough, there's always HRT to see them home and dry. Or rather, moist.

SIX

'You know what, John? I hate my job.'

Well, yes I did, actually. I'd have had to have been comatose not to. Every day my mate Alex and I chat on the phone for at least twenty minutes – yeah, blokes gossip too – and the last fortnight has turned into a non-stop moanathon. All that's changed is that the emotional temperature has risen from 'I don't like what I'm doing' through 'It's driving me mad' to the present 'I hate my job.'

'Why don't you leave, then?' I say in my best concerned, counsellorish voice, knowing full well it's about the least helpful thing I could possibly say. Because he can't leave. By most objective standards, Alex has a great job. It's interesting, it's creative, he's paid more than a Cabinet minister and there are hundreds of Alex wannabes out there desperate for what he's got. In fact, jobs don't come much better. So there's no point looking for another and he can't do nothing because he's got too many financial commitments. In short, he's trapped. Tee-hee.

'We went through that yesterday,' he replies carefully, completely oblivious to my attempt to wind him up. Which got me worried. When Alex misses a dig it means he's practically suicidal.

'Have you thought about ringing the Samaritans?' I say to cover myself. I wouldn't be able to live with myself if he went and topped himself and I hadn't done anything to help.

'Yeah, but they were engaged,' he answers, slightly recovering the will to live.

'Well, it's nice to know there's at least one other person in the same boat as you.'

Which was – as we both knew full well – a hell of an understatement. Because almost everyone we knew hated their job – if only a little bit. Some of them had really shitty jobs and had good reason to hate them, but then there were those like Alex for whom hate was a pathological response to any job he got. Go on, try him. Offer him anything you reckon to be nigh-on perfect and he'll loathe it within hours. Because he'll know that if he's been asked, it can't be worth doing.

This is one of the reasons Alex and I get on so well. We both know that somewhere along the line we've failed. It wasn't like this when we were in our thirties because we could both fool ourselves that we were on a journey and the proverbial pot of gold – what a laughable idea that seems now. What were we expecting? To wake up one day and feel good? – was just around the corner. But now we're in our forties – Alex doesn't like to admit this; his CV still says thirty-nine. But he's forty-three. Honest. Much older than me – another reason why I like him – it's downhill all the way. Because we're pretty much doing what we thought would be fun, and, of course, most of the time it isn't.

Mind you, I'm not sure that either of us has much idea of what fun is. When I was a student it involved doing as little as possible, while dreaming of being incredibly famous and making stacks of money. I was never fully sure where the fame and money were going to come from, though. I had vague thoughts of being a pop star – indulging in desultory bouts of solo air guitar – I had no musical talent – not necessarily a hindrance, I know, but I have integrity, *moi* – and really the only thing I found remotely interesting about the rock business was the huge quantities of available drugs. And since I was already doing OK on that score, there didn't seem much point putting myself out.

What I must have imagined, I suppose, was that someone would come up to me one day and offer me a job – dosh and fame attached – just for being me. It sounds daft, but there you are. Some people seem to be born knowing exactly what they want to do, but I never really had a clue.

'What do you want to do?' my parents would ask me endlessly.

Absolutely nothing, would have been the honest answer, but this sort of nihilism was absolutely *verboten* in the Crace household.

'I don't really know,' I would whine.

At this point things could have gone a number of ways. They could have told me to bugger off out of the house until I did or they could have said, 'We know so-and-so who might be able to help find you something.' But as my dad was a vicar and my mum a marriage-guidance counsellor – you can see where I get all my empathy from – neither insults nor nepotism were viable options. So what we got instead was:

'Perhaps you should see a careers consultant.'

After the umpteenth bidding I finally bothered to go. Their report was the usual xeroxed 'John is very enthusiastic, capable and gets on well with people. He should do well as a lawyer/accountant/astronaut/nuclear physicist' they dish out to every moronic recluse. So naturally I ended up enthusiastically and capably getting on well with people by selling them ice-creams in Oxford Street.

I didn't get on so well with people when I answered an ad in the back of the *Standard* which read 'Financial Advisers wanted' and became an insurance salesman – even though it was a huge step in the right direction as far as my parents were concerned. They were dead impressed that I wore a suit to work. I wish the same could have been said for everyone else. Because what the job invariably entailed was trying to sell someone a policy they didn't want or need. And you were supposed to start with your friends.

'Hi, Barry, it's John. We haven't spoken for a while.'

'John. How nice to hear from you.'

It won't be.

'Yeah . . . Er . . . How's things?'

I never have found it easy to get to the point.

'Fine. How about you?'

'Great. Er, the reason I'm ringing you is because I've got this new job.'

'I didn't know you had an old one.'

Now this is where a job screws you up. Because normally I would call him a cunt and we would have a laugh. But now that I wanted something from him, I came over all feeble.

'You're right. It's certainly the first that I thought had potential,' I say earnestly.

'What is it then?' Barry asks, stifling what sounds suspiciously like a yawn.

'I'm a financial adviser.'

'You're what? Since when did you know anything about money?'

Since two days ago, actually.

'Well, I'm learning on the job,' I reply defensively. 'And what I'd like to do is to come and chat to you about your financial arrangements to see if there are any areas that I might be able to help you with.'

'Oh, my God,' he laughs. 'You're an insurance sales-man, aren't you?'

'It's one of the services I can offer.'

'You, an insurance salesman, John. Whoever would have thought it?'

As it happened, Barry was one of the decent ones. Most people would have just put the phone down at this point. He, at least, bothered to meet me for lunch – he paid – and actually listened to me drone on for ten minutes, before saying 'I'll think about it' – which even I could take as a 'No, and don't dare ever mention it again', so we could move on to a more general gossip about what various of our friends were up to.

'You know what you're doin' wrong,' said Mark, my manager, when I got back to the office. 'You're just not closin' them.' Mark came from an incredibly posh back-ground, but ever since he'd been workin' in insurance he'd taken to droppin' the final 'g' from all his words. And it seemed to work for him. He could close anyone. But even when I tried dropping my 'g's, I was still a lousy salesman.

I did persevere, though. I carried on until I had lost every friend I had ever had – usually having bankrupted them first. And then I was fired. There were some suc-cesses along the way. For instance, I proved a dab hand at selling rubbish policies to ex-girlfriends. I think this was because they were the only people I never felt the slightest guilt about ripping off. Bad form, I know. You're meant to be terribly understanding about your exes. 'Yes, we were terribly young – it just wasn't the right time – we should have always stayed just friends – you'll always mean a great deal to me.' Well, sod that. I've never forgiven any of my exes for anything. So, Sue, if you thought I was about to start being nice after you went off and slept with Mike, you can think again. I don't care if it was all fifteen years ago. No one gets away with making a mess of my heart like that.

Still, if it's any consolation to them, the other person whom I happened to successfully swindle was myself. It would be nice to report that this was an extremely complicated fraud that, despite a twelve-month trial, failed to secure a conviction. But unfortunately, it was just that I turned out to be as dim as the rest of the general public and managed to sell myself the worst possible policy to guarantee a mortgage. And I'm still paying it today.

From here it wasn't such a long haul to becoming a writer as one might expect. Once you've failed as an insurance salesman, you have precious few options left. My wife had mixed feelings about my change of career. Saying you were a writer had a certain snob value as far as she was concerned, and so she was less ashamed of me; but she couldn't see why I had to choose a career where I was likely to make even less money than I had before.

Surprisingly, though, the dosh began to trickle in. I think initially it had a lot to do with my surname. At the time, Jim Crace, a writer of far less talent, come to mention it, had just established himself as a prize-winning author, and I have a feeling that quite a few newspaper editors confused me with him. I would ring up with an idea, they would say, who are you? I would make my first name unintelligible and shout 'CRACE' very loudly, and they would say 'YES'. Mind you, I was only paid once as if I was Jim – which was curious really, as the piece ended up getting spiked.

But the thing is I never really felt as if I was getting anywhere – even when I was, if you see what I mean. I can remember being vaguely excited about one job where I was sent off to interview Robbie Coltrane on the set of *Cracker*. It seemed like a prestigious gig. But all I can remember about it is being verballed by Robert Carlyle, who was psyching himself up to play a skinhead, and being made to wait for hours in the Old Trafford car park before anyone could be bothered to open the trailer door and acknowledge my existence. And, ultimately, this is what work is all about. Everyone wants to have someone less important than them – not necessarily to order around, though that's part of it – but so that they can feel better than them.

And when you've reached your forties, you realize that you've probably gone as far in your working life as you're going to go. Take Tony Blair. The man has shaken hands with thousands of people he probably can't stand, to get to where he thought he wanted to be. Prime Minister, top dog. Right? Wrong. Because when you get to Prime Minister you realize just how little power you have compared with someone like Bill Clinton. So you have to toady to him, say ridiculous things like 'Bill is one of my very best friends' when you've only spoken to him for ten minutes, and be prepared to go along with starting World War III just to keep the President's dick off the news agenda. And that is about as good as it's ever going to get. In a few years' time he will be the ex-PM and no one will give a toss about him any more. And if his hair continues to fall out at the same rate, no one will even recognize him.

Mind you, it must be even worse to be John Prescott. Knowing that you're too fat, too ugly, and too principled ever to get the top job. Imagine a lifetime in politics and not even getting where you wanted. How he must envy Tony Blair. I wonder if he has dreams of Tony coming to a sticky end and him getting the invite from the Queen to be PM. Well, I've got news for you, John. You would only ever be an interim measure – Peter Mandelson would make sure of that.

Don't get me wrong, I'm not exactly miserable about what I do. I'd like a few more perks – well, any really. Like having underlings. But working freelance doesn't tend to give that. I suppose that's one of the reasons for having children. Someone to shout at. But a lot of the time I don't mind what I do. Until I start to think about it. Then I realize that I'm living a *Groundhog Day* existence, repeating myself *ad nauseam*, and the only thing that's changing – details apart – is that I'm getting older.

Maybe I missed something somewhere. I thought that a job was supposed to be important, provide meaning.

Because to me a job sure can't just be about the money. If it was I'd be off selling crack or working in the City. The primary function of a job is to be a job. It's a way of filling up the day to keep you more or less occupied. To stop you thinking about what you would be doing if you didn't have a job. Which you won't one day. And no one will care that much, because, although you might like to think you're irreplaceable, you're not. Someone else will come along and do it equally well. Perhaps better.

Ultimately, a job is just a means of keeping people off the streets for a few years, a way of stopping everyone going round trying to kill one another. Except, of course, for those jobs, such as the army, where that's precisely what you're trained for. The only real value a job has is what each person ascribes to it, to make themselves feel better about their life. And once you know that, you're fucked. You can't stop doing what you're doing, because you're doing better than others you can think of and because it's even more desperate to imagine yourself doing nothing, but carrying on becomes an exercise in futility. What you've always wanted turns out to have been an illusion.

It's at this point that some people start to think about becoming a therapist. Think of our great leader, Tony Blair. The man acts like a counsellor rather than a politician. He preaches and he's developed a style of speaking that shows he really understands our pain. And believe me, he hasn't done this because he thinks it's politically effective. It's happening to him in spite of himself. He's a man so riven with an internal sense of nothingness that he is metamorphosing into a complete know-all in front of our eyes.

After all, what is more tempting for someone who is dealing with their own life failures than to spend time and take money off people who are dealing with theirs. That way, you automatically become less of a failure than them. And you can pass this all off under the guise of helping people. Imagine it.

'So tell me a little about what's going on?'

'I've lost my job and my girlfriend's shagging David Mellor.'

Fantastic. Thank God my life's not that bad.

'And how does that feel?'

'Pretty dreadful.'

Can't let him get away with that. Better rub his nose in it.

'Only pretty dreadful. It sounds as though you feel it's worse than that.'

'You're right. It's absolutely terrible, actually. What shall I do?'

'What do you think you should do?'

'I dunno. That's why I'm asking you.'

'We've run out of time now, but we'll deal with why you expect me to provide all the answers next week. That's £35 please.'

Before you get carried away and start up your own private practice, do remember there are some drawbacks.

Hanging out with losers the whole time can be depressing. Imagine having to listen to someone like me wittering on about my pitiful little life. Personally, I can think of nothing worse. Which, come to think of it, is why I'll stick to what I'm doing.

SEVEN

'Er, hello, John,' says Keith shiftily, as he hurriedly shovels assorted drugs and several items of related paraphernalia under a magazine.

Parties are just no fun at my age. I used to feel confident about walking into any room – even one with a bunch of strangers, because I felt in control. If I was made to feel welcome – you knew you were allowed to stay if someone offered you some narcs – then fine, and if not, well who cared when you had a pocketful of your own anyway?

But nowadays – on the rare occasions when I get invited anywhere – I tend to stay put in the kitchen and hang around with the other losers who are too frightened to go anywhere else. I know my place. I'm one of the grown-ups who are tolerated so long as they don't stray off limits. But now and then you need the bathroom. For a piss, mind – nothing exotic. And you run the risk of bumping into someone like Keith, whom you've met a couple of times through a friend at work and who is at least ten years younger than you.

'Hi, Keith,' I say as nonchalantly as possible. Which was quite difficult as I wasn't really sure whether the coolest way to play it lay in letting him know that I knew what he was up to and was completely blasé about it, or ignoring the whole thing.

'Good to see you, man,' he replies, lying through his teeth, as he looks up anxiously. I think he was seriously concerned I might make a citizen's arrest. Which wasn't such a bad idea, come to think of it. So watch out.

'Good to see you, too,' I say, lying through mine.

I hate myself sometimes. Well, most of the time actually. Why am I such a wimp? Why did I have to take the soft option of pretending not to notice the gear, and leave myself open to this sort of mindless exchange from which there's only ever one winner. And no prizes for guessing who that was going to be.

'How are you doing?'

'Fine. How about you?'

'Fine.'

Oh really? Well, you don't look it. You've got sweat pouring off you, your eyes are popping out of their sockets and your nose is dripping blood.

'Er. Are you going to be long? I'm desperate for a piss.'

'Umm, I'm a bit tied up. Can you hang on a minute?'

'Sure.'

How pathetic can you get. I want a piss and he doesn't. He's in the lav and I'm not. And I'm the one who's got to wait.

A couple of minutes later Keith appeared and muttered something sheepish like 'Thanks for waiting, man.'

'Man'. Why is it that some people only have to see a Rizla and they start calling you 'man'?

'No problem.'

No problem? Just listen to me. What I really mean is, why don't you have a heart attack, fall down the stairs and choke on your own vomit?

Can you believe it? Here's a bloke who's out of his head on coke and I'm jealous. Or is it envious, I'm never sure which. I mean, coke, for God's sake. The most overrated, pointless drug ever made, and I'm wishing that I had some. What's going on?

What's going on is that I've reached an age – well, truthfully, I probably reached it ten years ago – where I can't go around behaving like a twat any more. My body can't handle the punishment and my mind can't cope with being permanently scrambled. Besides which, drugs are a young person's kind of thing. I mean, what do you think when you see some forty year-old advertising exec cartwheeling around the room out of his head trying to dance to Radiohead? You think, sad git, that's what.

Take William Burroughs. A few literary types who can't see further than the end of their own syringes see him as something of a literary genius. How absurd can you get. The man was only famous for being a junky and shooting someone – I can't remember who – and he wrote one moderately interesting book about being – guess what? – a junky. After that he just churned out a whole heap of nonsense that nobody had the balls to challenge. I'm not saying the man didn't have talent. He just never stopped taking drugs for long enough to allow anyone to find out.

The trouble is that part of me still thinks taking drugs is pretty cool. I know it's ridiculous, but there you are. I can't help it. Which, I suppose, is why I have come to hate all people who take them. All this let's legalize cannabis, let's decriminalize heroin stuff we're getting these days really annoys me. As far as I'm concerned, if it's not OK for me, then it's not OK for anyone else. That's it. No exceptions. Instead of this new wishy-washy liberalism we're beginning to see peddled about the place, let's get punitive. How about the death penalty for possession of any class of drug? Or life imprisonment at the very least. We'd certainly be seeing a few more scumbags going cold turkey, then.

Umm. That last bit. You don't think it was a bit over the top, do you? Well, maybe a touch. But keep it to yourself, please. Our little secret. Because that's obviously not what I say in public. Coming on all hard-line gets you labelled as a psychopath or a possible Tory candidate.

Either way, you lose a lot of friends. And I can't afford to lose any more. So naturally I've developed a much more sympathetic persona to explain this stance. It goes something like, 'I reached a point where I realized I was going to have to stop using drugs. I found they just weren't fun any more, and they were interfering with my life. But I've no objection to them in principle. So please, carry on and roll up if you want to.' Pretty good, huh? Just call me Johnny Sincerity.

If you want to make the successful transition from drug user to non-drug user, you have to find a way of maintaining your credibility. The aim is to let it be casually known that you were once very, very hard indeed. That you once consumed your whole supply for a three-day festival in an afternoon. That you've had your stomach pumped more times than they've had hot dinners. That sort of thing.

But the telling has to be done carefully, because there's a narrow dividing line between being very, very hard and being very, very stupid. And most people get it hopelessly wrong. Once, when I was serving my drug apprenticeship – you know, that period where you're learning to roll a joint without the thing coming to bits in your hands. I was hopeless. All fingers and thumbs. Plus my hands would get all trembly. Especially if any girls were around – I came across some old hippie who had clearly been using for years. And, believe it or not, I was prepared to be deeply impressed. And I was, initially. Until he opened his mouth and started babbling on about tripping to Hawkwind at the Windsor free festival and smoking dope backstage at a Genesis concert. Then I just thought, moron.

And people are still getting it wrong today. Look at that bloke Howard Marks – the so-called Mr Nice. The man must be at least fifty and all he can do is drone on and on about how much dope he has smuggled and how he was really just trying to do everyone a favour. Yeah, peace and love to you too, Howie. I mean, what a complete fucking waste of a life. Just imagine what it must be like talking to him.

'Tell me, Howard. What have you been up to recently?'

'I've been in prison.'

'Oh dear.'

'Yeah, it was really heavy. The pigs got me for running dope.'

'Well, what did you expect?'

'What do you mean, man?'

'I mean, you smuggled dope, you got caught, you went to prison. A child of ten could have worked that one out.'

'Yeah, but the system's so unfair, man.'

It's at about this point in the conversation that you become terminally bored. And then it's up to you to do something, because the chances are that our Howard will be so full of himself that he won't have the sensitivity to realize he's dribbling, repeating himself and generally being a total waste of space. So it's just a question of whether you decide to kill him or yourself. For God's sake, Howard, pull yourself together. Get your hair cut and join the army or something. Just stop embarrassing yourself. I ask you. Some people have no sense of shame.

But let's just assume – for the sake of argument – that you are one of the lucky few who can make it into middle age without becoming a complete joke to all those younger than you. I'm talking hypothetically here. Obviously. I thought that I had better get that in before you did. Anyway, the point is that you're still far from sorted. Because you've still got to learn how to talk to people.

You see, drugs are the perfect antidote to conversation. Tense? Nervous? Pop something. Anything. Once you're safely cocooned in a world of your own, then nothing else really matters. If you've done a few lines of speed or coke, you will have no qualms about drivelling on about nothing in particular while you sweetly imagine you're being utterly fascinating. And if you're stoned, then you're generally happy sitting around communing with the wallpaper. Either way, the good news is that you don't have to feel anything. And when you don't feel anything, then no one can get to you.

Tell me I'm a useless, ugly, balding git these days and I'll obsess about it endlessly. Actually, I won't, since you'll only be telling me something I already know. But say the same thing to someone who's out of their head and it'll be dismissed with a shrug. Because drugs give you that inner glow of Ready Brek superiority. Somehow you just know that you're right and everyone else is wrong. Users call it having a raised level of consciousness. Which shows how deluded you can get.

Here's a thing. You can scarcely move for women saying how remote men are and how they long for someone emotionally available. 'You just can't get one anywhere, darling. Not even at Harvey Nicks.' So how come you go to a party and the blokes who are moody, aloof and can't string a sentence together are surrounded by women? Either the women just like the idea of an available man rather than the real McCoy, or they can't resist a challenge. Or they're just hoping for some free dope.

This last option has always seemed much the most likely to me. I've always been amazed at how bored people are prepared to be if they think there's going to be a few free jollies at the end of it. Why else would anyone willingly spend time with a coke freak? How desperate. All those people putting on their Fleetwood Mac albums in the hope that Stevie Nicks or Lindsay Buckingham would come toddling through the door and share their stash with them.

No wonder so many blokes end up on drugs. It's the only way you're guaranteed to get laid. And if you aren't stoned but hang around looking as if you are, you might at least get a snog before the girl realizes you've got absolutely nothing she wants. Image counts for a lot, because no girl wants a Mr Clean-and-Reliable. Except when it comes to getting married. And that's a whole new ball game.

What little success I ever had with women in my youth was entirely down to a bloke called John. Honest. That was his name. Not only did he teach me how to differentiate between various drugs, he showed me how to get by without talking to women. You just sat around doing some gear and waited for women to approach you. You then said absolutely nothing other than a dreamy 'Hi', followed by 'Do you want some?' if you really fancied them. It was the perfect system because you never had to run the risk of rejection. If she didn't fancy you she would bugger off pretty smartish and she would only be able to hazard a guess as to whether you had the hots for her. And the longer she stayed the more obvious she would invariably become, until you had frustrated her into submission. Eventually she would crack and say, 'Do you want to go to bed with me?' 'Christ, I thought you would never ask,' was not a popular reply. One of the things I am most proud of is that I have never asked a woman to go to bed with me. Sometimes I may have had to be a bit subtle and lay a trail of drugs along the carpet from the living-room to the bedroom, but I have never had to say the words. Come to think of it, perhaps that's why so many of my exes were junkies. Only joking, Julia.

This approach to picking up women does have something of a downside, as you can never be certain how many opportunities you've let slip, but on the whole it's a fair trade-off for never having to hear the words 'You are the most revolting person I've ever met. I would rather die than fuck you.' But unfortunately, once you stop taking drugs you still have the emotional age of a prepubescent. So there you are, a balding grown-up completely at a loss as to what to say to someone of the opposite sex. Perhaps you might have got lucky and found a partner in your drug days, so aren't on the lookout for nookie, but it's still a nightmare.

Some blokes avoid having nothing to say by just moving straight on to the booze. I suppose they reckon the bulbous nose, the expanding gut and the unfortunate trouser stains are a price worth paying for their social intercourse. But I'm not so sure. Which makes life tricky. Because what are you supposed to say and how do you say it without sounding like you're at a job interview? Do you launch into 'Hello, who are you, what do you do?' or do you try something more risky like 'What did you think of the Budget?', which might leave you having to conjure up an intelligent view of your own, pronto. And how can you tell if that glazed look in your victim's eyes is a sign that she needs urgent hospital attention or is just plain bored? Search me.

I had thought there was going to be an upside to this drug-free lifestyle. For one thing, I mused, my relationship with my wife must improve, and for another, I would have loads of spare dosh. Wrong on both counts.

The relationship first. Now, technically speaking – which when you're talking feelings means therapeutically speaking – I suppose I have to concede that the relationship did improve, in that it became more meaningful. Any shrink would have given us ten out of ten for our willingness to deal with stuff. For those unfamiliar with the terminology, 'stuff' is a very precise therapeutic term for lots of issues. And you can look up 'issues' yourself. But all this is a long way from saying that it got better. Because we started to argue non-stop.

'I'm just going to put Van Morrison on the CD,' she said provocatively.

'You can't,' I replied.

'Why not?'

'Because I hate it.'

'Well, I don't,' she said unreasonably.

'But it's bollocks. It's just about tolerable if you're completely stoned, but straight, it's unlistenable.'

'I don't care what you think. I'm putting it on anyway.' And she did.

Just listen to her. She doesn't care what I think. How much of this sort of thing did I let her get away with when I was stoned? It's a pity I can't remember, but I have a suspicion that it was an awful lot. Time to put my foot down.

'I'm taking this off and putting some Schubert on instead.'

'You're fucking not.'

'I am. Listen. I like Schubert, you like Schubert. I hate Van Morrison, you like Van Morrison. Ergo, you listen to Van Morrison when I'm not around.'

Sometimes my logistical brilliance astounds me.

But not her.

'You're not going to tell me what to do.'

'Why not?' probably wasn't going to be the most sensible answer under the circumstances. Ah, to hell with it.

'Why not?'

It's best to draw a veil over what happened next. Just let's say it became childish and abusive.

This argument wasn't a one-off, and it developed many sophisticated variations. But the theme was always the same. The absence of drugs had altered the status quo at home, and I was no longer prepared to be so compliant to my wife's wishes. She, needless to say, took this as a descent into fascism and fogyism on my part, but it wasn't that straightforward. It was more that, having wasted so much of my life up till then, I was buggered if I was going to waste any more. Especially on the likes of Van Morrison.

All this costs money, which is where the added expense of not using drugs comes in. Because all sorts of records and other cultural goodies you were quite proud of while you were using suddenly become horrendously embarrassing. So you have to replace them all with something worthwhile.

Many people are too mean to do this. This is a big mistake, because you end up in a corner having to pretend that you really still like the same things you used to. Even the richest people sometimes do this. Look at Eric Clapton. The man's a multimillionaire, but what has he done since coming off the booze and drugs? He's just continued to turn out the same dreary tosh as before. He can't possibly be enjoying it. What a crying shame. If only he'd had the self-worth to spend a few thousand quid on a new record collection, he could have really made something of himself.

By new record collection, I really mean old record collection. You know classical. Everyone tells me that I've become an old fart, but as far as I'm concerned not having to listen to pop music is the only benefit to getting older I've yet discovered. And it's a great deal less embarrassing for a forty-year-old to buy a Beethoven string quartet than a Portishead album. Ask my wife. I'm sorry, that was a bit disloyal. Never mind. Poor old Portishead. The band would pack up today if they had any idea that forty-year-olds were into them.

But let's forget about all the cultural reasons for abandoning drugs as you get older. In many ways they're only a side issue. The most compelling reason for not using is to give yourself something to look forward to when you're really old. Like on the way out. Think about it. At least one in three people are going to die of cancer. It could be you. Or me. And what are you going to do about it? I know what I've got planned.

'Mr Crace, I've got some very bad news, I'm afraid. You've got an inoperable tumour.'

'Oh dear. Can I have some morphine then?'

'Are you in a lot of pain?'

'Massive.'

'OK then. How much do you want?'

'How much have you got?'

Now, if you were still using, news that you were terminally ill could be terribly depressing. Do it my way, and every cloud has a silver lining. Who says it doesn't pay to think ahead?

EIGHT

'Daddy?'

'Yes.'

'Wassat?'

'What's what?'

'That,' said Tom, pointing at the lawnmower.

'It's a lawnmower.'

Pause.

'Daddy?'

'Yes.'

'Wassat?'

'What's what?'

'That,' said Tom, pointing at the lawnmower.

'It's still a lawnmower, darling,' I answered irritably.

Pause.

'Daddy?'

'Ye-es.'

'Wassat?'

'That,' said Tom, pointing to the lawnmower.

'IT'S A FRIGGING LAWNMOWER, FOR GOD'S SAKE.'

Pause.

'Daddy?'

'Yes.'

'What's frigging?'

If I hadn't already been through exactly the same sort of conversation – if you can call it that – with my daughter, Jo, when she was Tom's age, I'd be seriously worried that our two-year-old son was as dim as they come. His capacity to retain the simplest piece of information – other than the words 'sword' and 'cartoons' – remains so completely non-existent that I think he's genuinely surprised to find himself in the same house when he wakes up in the morning.

The social worker – sorry, health visitor – sees it a little differently. She insists that Tom is quite normal and his endless questions, such as 'Who am I?', are signs of a lively, enquiring mind. Which sounds suspiciously like special pleading to me. When I was a kid, if a grown-up told you something was a lawnmower, you bloody well remembered it was a lawnmower. Otherwise you were soundly thrashed. All this 'be nice to kids, let them find things out for themselves' is just another excuse for falling standards.

And there's a disturbing knock-on effect to all this

interaction. While you're busy letting your little treasure get away with merry hell because it's part of the growing-up process, the little brat is working away at a completely different agenda. Because the primary purpose of every child is to grind its parents into the dirt.

'You know, John. Having children really helps to keep you young.' This was one of the stranger remarks that my mother made to me shortly after Jo was born, as even in my highly frazzled, demented state I could see it was complete bollocks. I mean, what could she have been thinking of? Her hair went grey in her thirties and, as far as I can see, it's been downhill ever since. I suppose it's conceivable that her own childhood could have been so unhappy that enduring her three children's seemed like a doddle in comparison. If so, the poor woman deserves a lot of sympathy after what we put her through.

But I suppose one needs this sort of myth about children, otherwise no one would ever bother to become a parent. Except by accident. Because all parents invariably decide to have children when they realize:

a) they've gone as far in their careers as they're going to get;

or

b) they want to be treated seriously by their own parents;

or

c) they can't think of anything better to do with their lives.

So naturally they want to believe everything is going to be fun, exciting, new and – above all – young. Children become an expression of immortality.

Confession time. I fell for all this. I really did. Hook, line and sinker. I believed that children were going to revitalise me and provide a new direction in my life. And I wasn't wholly wrong. It's just that I hadn't appreciated that the direction would be inexorably down.

Everyone knows that teenagers think their parents are fuckwits, but what most don't realize is that this attitude actually starts at birth. Children are predisposed to replace their parents. We're talking serious pathology here. Because by 'replace' I mean 'kill'.

Take the new-born baby screaming in the night. One interpretation is that it's hungry and a bit lonely, and wants some milk and a cuddle. Which is exactly what it wants you to think, as you get lulled into a feeling of 'poor, defenceless darling' and 'what a great parent I am to be able to give it what it needs'. But there's something much more sinister going on. All this crying is designed to exhaust the parents. The little bastard waits until you've just dozed off and then yells, 'Waah.' And after it's done this two or three times a night, then you're out on your feet.

Which is no skin off the infant's nose, since he or she can catch up on a few zeds during the daytime. But you can't, as you have to go to work. So the decline starts immediately. You're so knackered you can't do your job properly, so you can kiss goodbye to any hope of promotion. That's it. Your life's over. Sometimes literally. Because what your child is really hoping is that you'll fall asleep on the M1 and total yourself and the car. That's the jackpot. And if you think that this is self-defeating for the child as there's no one left to look after it, then you'd better wise up sharpish. Children have evolved. These days they're born knowing all about welfare benefits and foster-parents.

What I'm not so sure about is how Oedipal this all is. I'm fairly certain that new-borns aren't too fussy about which parent gets knocked off, and even as they get older the death of either parent is a major victory. But there certainly comes an age at which – if the children were allowed to express a preference – the killing would get divided up along gender lines. Boys want to kill their dads and girls want to kill their mums.

Jo, being the eldest, was the first to show these urges.

'I want my mummy.'

'What's the matter, sweetie?' I said, rushing towards her.

'I want my mummy.'

'It's OK. I'm here.'

'I don't want you. Want Mummy.'

'Mummy's upstairs.'

Plenty howls, followed by:

'I want my mummy.'

'Just tell me what's wrong.'

'No. I want my mummy.'

At this point, my wife came shooting down the stairs trying to look concerned, while doing her best to conceal how smug she was feeling.

'Come and tell Mummy what's wrong, darling,' she said cloyingly.

'I don't feel very well.'

For a long time I used to get pissed off by this. Jo feels ill, Jo shouts for Mummy, and Daddy feels inferior, redundant and worthless. Until I realized that Jo was doing me a favour. She knew she had a collection of virulent – perhaps deadly – germs, and she wanted to make sure that it was Mummy who got them. Giving me a wide berth was her way of protecting me and saying, 'You're more important to me than Mummy.' It wasn't quite so funny when Tom started shouting, 'I love you, Daddy' when he had a chest infection.

Apart from illness, children get few opportunities to mount assassination attempts on their parents. It's one of the drawbacks to being a dwarf. Thank God. Still, this hasn't prevented Jo from having a go. The most recent example was at her sports day. Just as my wife was lining up for the start of the mothers' race, Jo shouted out, 'Come on, Mummy. I want you to win.' An idiot would take this as a child wanting to take pride in its parent. The real message, though, was 'I know you haven't taken any exercise for donkey's years and I'm trying to shame you into overdoing it so you drop down dead halfway up the finishing straight.'

By and large, children are merely engaged in a war of attrition with their parents.

'Daddy?'

'Yes.'

'I wanna fly my kite in the park.'

'But there's no wind.'

'I don't care.'

'But it just won't fly. It's pointless.'

'Oh, go on, Daddy. P-leeeeze.'

So you end up going because you think you'll be a lousy dad if you don't. And, of course, the kite doesn't even get a centimetre off the ground.

'Make it fly, Daddy.'

'I can't. There's no wind.'

Like I said, if you'd bothered to listen.

'But I want it to fly.'

'It's not going to.'

'Katie's daddy got her kite to fly.'

'It was probably windy, then.'

'I think you're useless, Daddy.'

Which is what the whole charade has been building up to. It hasn't been about the kite, it's been about getting you to realize how useless you are. The same thing goes for Jo and her bicycle. When she says she wants to go for a ride, she doesn't really mean it. What she wants is for you to follow her on foot for five minutes so that she can say she's bored and get you to carry or push the bike back home.

Everything is designed to make you feel worthless. You look back on your day and think, What the fuck have I been doing? What you've been doing is running around organizing your children to do nothing in particular, and then clearing up after them when they've done it. And it's all been utterly pointless. Any image that you might have had of yourself as a competent, successful and productive member of society – apparently there are people who feel, or have felt, like this – is systematically eroded. You have become a machine. Even worse, you have become a very old machine.

And your children have no compunction about letting you know it. They get away with it , too, as their ruthless honesty is always excused as charming naivety. Which it isn't. It's just another form of their natural sadism.

'Daddy?'

I hate being interrupted while I'm in the bath at the best of times, but when it's one of the kids you just know it's going to be aggravation.

'What?'

You've got to try to be nice to them.

'What are those white bits in your hair?'

Ah, the white bits. Like you really don't know. Like you haven't asked me about them hundreds of times before.

' They're not white bits, darling. They're grey hairs.'

'Oh. Why are they grey?'

'It happens when you get old.'

Jo has got the next bit off pat. She knows just how to inflect the killer punch with the appropriate level of innocent surprise for maximum effect.

'Ah, I see. You mean like Granny and Grandad.'

Gritted-teeth time.

'Hmm. That sort of thing.'

It won't come as a big shock to you to discover that my wife relishes these exchanges between Jo and me. Because she doesn't have any grey hairs. Mincing Carl, who charges her £80 to fawn over her head for an hour and a half, sees to that. And for her it really is a case of out of sight out of mind, because she has completely obliterated any memory of her hair being anything other than its natural, highlighted colour.

Mind you, that's not to say that she doesn't have her Achilles' heel. Not that I would ever dare mention it out loud. Which is where having children can come in useful, for once. A quick 'Jo, whatever you do, don't go and annoy Mummy while she's getting dressed by asking her about her stretch marks' does the trick every time.

And it's not just kids who make you feel geriatric.

'And you are. . .?'

It was Jo's first day at school and I was meeting her form-teacher for the first time.

'I'm Jo's father.'

'Oh. Mr Crace. Of course,' she said doubtfully. Miss Richards – as both Jo and I were expected to call her – was in her early twenties. As such, she was a great deal closer to

Jo's age than to mine. And it showed. She clearly thought I was just some nondescript grown-up. Over the age of forty everyone starts to look the same to young people, and presumably I could just as easily have been Jo's grandfather as her dad. And Miss Richards, ever the diplomat, hadn't wanted to risk getting it wrong. Take a chance next time – eh?

I don't want you to get the wrong impression here. I'm not anti-kids. I'm not some bloke who was coerced against his will into procreation, as many men of my acquaintance seem to have been. 'So-and-so was a bit of an accident' and 'It was a hell of a surprise' have become familiar refrains over the years, but, forgive me if I'm missing something, no one has ever had an accidental shag with me, more's the pity, and even if they had, a baby wouldn't be a particularly surprising outcome. A winning lottery ticket? Maybe. True love? Definitely. But a baby? Hardly.

No, I had my eyes wide open – though not necessarily at the moment of conception – about having kids. I knew they were going to be difficult little sods from the off, but I figured there would be a trade-off. And the trade-off was going to be that I could get to do all those things I had fancied doing as a kid but was never allowed to. More importantly, I could get to do it without looking a prat, as I could pretend I was only doing it for my children's benefit.

This is where having a son really helped. Much as I loved Jo, she was just never interested in balls or Action

Men. I tried to make her. I really did. But she was peculiarly resistant. It was as if she had some inbuilt toy detector that could pick up the slightest sign of gender bias in any given object, and anything that wasn't obviously girlie was summarily dismissed. And while this was fine for my wife, it wasn't for me, since I'd never had the slightest Barbie fantasy as a boy. OK, that's not exactly true. I must own up to a slight *frisson* the first time I ever got her kit off – but it was only a passing thing, you understand.

But Tom was a bit different. Unlike Jo, who has always had this really weedy throw that all girlies seem to have, Tom had more of a bloke's delivery from the word go. What's more, he was dead keen on Action Men. But oddly enough, the more he enjoyed them, the less I did. Here I was with enough money to buy myself a whole platoon of the new beefier plastic hunks – something I would have killed for as a child – and I couldn't really be bothered.

Now, I suppose that you could interpret this as one of the few outward signs that I had emotionally matured a little. But to me it was a real let-down. While I'm all for a bit of emotional maturity in others – my wife and friends, especially – some hope – I consider it to be an overrated virtue in myself. Because it's like a part of you dying – the part that is young and lively. And all that's left is the disappointment.

Football was a case in point. Now, I was lucky. Tom was born supporting Spurs, so there was no family feuding. He even insisted on having a replica shirt. 'My Tottnam,' he called it. But when push came to shove, I couldn't get too worked up about the whole thing. The main problem was that the players didn't mean anything to me. When I was a kid, the names Greaves, Gilzean, Jennings and Mullery had resonance. The men were gods. But Armstrong, Berti, Walker and Ginola are bog-standard through and through. Especially Ginola.

'You're jealous of him,' said my wife cheerfully. Having never shown the slightest interest in footie for years and years, she'd joined the massed ranks of women who had suddenly decided that they were now hard-core fans. Of course, this was because, like the others, she had found that the game had been made much more accessible to women. And nothing whatsoever to do with the fact that soccer players were now being sold as sex on legs. So she was naturally unable to tell me a single worthwhile fact about her David, as she referred to him, other than what car he drove, what designer suits he wore and the name of his hair stylist.

'Jealous of Ginola?' I protested. 'How can you be jealous of the bloke who single-handedly put France out of the 1994 World Cup?'

'Yes, you are,' she pounced. 'You hate it that there's someone drop-dead gorgeous playing for your team.'

'Oh. So he's drop-dead gorgeous now, is he?'

'Well. Yeah. What's so strange about that?'

Ah. It's become a fact. There's no question of doubt. The world is round. Ginola is drop-dead gorgeous.

'It's just that you've never called anyone else drop-dead gorgeous before.'

Like me, for instance.

'I've never said that you aren't drop-dead gorgeous,' she countered, though with not nearly enough grovelling. Or sincerity.

'How wonderfully reassuring. You've never said that Quasimodo isn't drop-dead gorgeous either.'

'Oh, do belt up.'

'Why should I?' I replied. 'It's thoroughly depressing to hear that your wife fancies someone who looks absolutely nothing like you. I mean, the bloke looks like an extra out of *Friends*.'

'You mean he's got hair and you haven't.'

'I have got hair.'

A bit.

'But for how long?' she muttered under her breath.

She was walking all over me. What was up? I must have been more jealous than I thought. Come on, John, fight back.

'Don't you think there's something fundamentally sad about a woman lusting after air-brushed footballers half her age?'

'For God's sake, stop going on and on about it. It's just a harmless piece of fun,' she snapped. 'It's not as if I'm planning to seduce him.'

No. But it's not as if I'm planning on seducing Kylie Minogue either. Though I am open to offers, Kylie. But if I drone on and on about how much I fancy her, I get labelled as some desperate middle-aged git who's trying to come on all laddish. When my wife gets all twittery about that berk Ginola, then obviously she's really making some post-modern ironic feminist statement.

But that's just the way it goes, I guess. At least our little fantasies give us something to talk about, as pretty soon we're going to need to become experts at talking to one another. Because the kids are rapidly getting to the age when they will only communicate in grunts.

Silent, sullen teenagers. There's something to look forward to. Having ruthlessly made sure that you've got absolutely no friends left who can bare to spend more than twenty minutes in your house, your children then become Trappists. So you end up living in a world of sensory deprivation, with only TV for company. Apart from your wife, that is. And you can't rely on her.

'I'm thinking of getting a dog,' she said the other day, knowing full well that I hate them. Still, I suppose it's marginally preferable to David bloody Ginola.

NINE

Look at me. My skin sags, my face is lined – well beyond the handsomely rugged stage – and my gut bulges. I'm a physical wreck.

It's just not fair. I was never meant to be like this. I was meant to be thin, athletic and brimful of testosterone, pheromones and all sorts of other blokish hormonal goodies. And I don't even feel as if it's my fault that I'm not. OK, I wasn't very nice to my body in my younger days, but for the last eleven years I've lived like a saint. Believe me, I've been counting the days. In fact, perversely, I used to look quite well preserved when I was abusing my system. But then maybe the drugs I was taking were cut with formalin. Whatever. As soon as I started treating my body like a temple, it decided to start treating me with utter contempt.

My body is a traitor. Plain and simple. I know that betrayal is an ugly word, but the truth isn't always that pleasant. My body is Philby, Burgess and Maclean all rolled into one.

You see, there's a point where your body stops being your friend and turns into your implacable enemy. And the biggest mistake anyone can make is to ignore this, by passing it off with 'It's part of the ageing process' and an affected Gallic shrug. Because this is what your body wants you to do. It wants you to believe that it and your mind are part of the same entity and that what's happening is totally out of your control.

Which it isn't necessarily, as long as you realize just how cunning your body can be. When you reach an age where you need to do a load of exercise to keep in shape, it deliberately breaks down. Try to do too much running, and your knees give out. Trust me. The voice of experience speaks. Plus your body controls your eyes so that you only see what's really what when it's far too late. This makes most people suffer from delayed reaction. You see the reflection of the person you were six months ago, and so you chug along quite happily, thinking all's well until, BOOM, one day you look in the mirror and there's this vaguely familiar fat person staring back. It gets worse, because the time delay means you're actually six months fatter than the fat person you're looking at.

There's no getting away from it. Your body is a nasty bastard whose one aim in life is to fuck you up. And your mind has to be every bit as devious if it is going to take it on.

Some people pretend to be delighted with the change in their physical appearance. 'We're all far too obsessed with body image,' they go on. 'I feel totally comfortable with the way I am.' Clearly, the hope is that your body will be listening intently to all this and will say to itself, 'Oh, comfortable, are you? I'll soon put a stop to that.' And make you thin again. Well, I've got news for you. It doesn't work, because your body isn't that easily conned. It knows that no one really wants to be fat. Given the choice between being fat and being thin, nobody says, 'Ooh, I want to waddle around the place out of breath and only be able to guess where my feet are.'

'Hi, John.'

'Hi, Mike.'

A phone call from Mike is always welcome. He's turned himself into a country bumpkin and manages to make me feel that I have an exciting, groovy metropolitan lifestyle. Rather than the suburban plod that it is.

'I was in London the other day doing some shopping on the King's Road and I couldn't find anything that fitted.'

What a surprise. Mike makes me look like I've got hair and am thin with it. That's another thing that I like about him.

'Evans must have closed down then.'

Where fat's concerned, no one is getting any sympathy from me. If I'm going down, then I'm taking everyone else with me.

'Oh, fuck off.'

'Well, really. What did you expect? You're twice the size and twice the age of everyone else on the King's Road.'

'But you've got to make an effort, haven't you?'

Yes. You have. But not like that. There's nothing your body wants more than you to squeeze into clothes that are too tight and too young for you, and for the rest of the world to have a good old snigger as you potter about making a prat of yourself.

That's not to say that I don't understand Mike's problem; it's just that it's one of the few I don't suffer from. Though I can't take any credit for this. You see, Mike was a snappy dresser. Once. So there's something he's trying to live up to. I've never been stylish, though. Not for want of trying, mind. I'm as vain as they come about loads of things. But clothes and me have never been *simpatico*. I can recognize what looks good on others – sometimes – but whenever I've tried to wear something similarly fashionable, I feel all wrong.

At heart, I'm just a Marks & Spencer kind of guy – even though some of their designs have been bordering on the dangerously racy in the last few years. But that's where I shop. From head to toe, I'm M&S man. Socks, undies, jeans, trousers, T-shirts, shirts and sweaters – all in various drab hues. Oh, I nearly forgot. I've also got an M&S suit. For those really special occasions.

My clothes are dull. I make no bones about it. Even I

find them boring. But that's good. Because my body hates them. It loathes the fact that I can get away with wearing the same sort of clothes now as I could ten or fifteen years ago because I've remained equally unremarkable. So for what it's worth, here's my hot fashion tip. Start as you will have to go on and make the most of being dreary. You won't regret it, I promise.

This might seem like an awful amount of effort to put into one's sartorial inelegance, but any victory – however minor – over your body is not to be sniffed at. You need to be full-on in the battle against its treachery at all times. Most importantly, you have to keep your body engaged and focused on the trivial for as long as possible. For if it gets so much as a whiff that you're tiring of the struggle, it will have no qualms about committing the ultimate betrayal. Which is to stop working completely.

'Oi, John. Have you heard about Paul?'

There was an urgency in Alex's voice that suggested this wasn't your average gossip.

'What about him?'

'He's dead.'

'You're kidding.'

'No. He's fucking dead.'

'How?'

A caring person would probably have said, 'That's terrible. His poor family' at this point. But 'how' was all that really mattered to me.

'I dunno for certain. His girlfriend just found him dead

in the living-room. They reckon it must have been a heart attack.'

This was the answer I had been dreading. Up till then all the friends that I'd known who had died had pegged out doing something dim, such as falling off a motor bike, ODing on smack or topping themselves. Which had been OK. Ish. I'd been upset, I missed them, but it wasn't hard to distance myself from the manner of their death. I didn't ride a motor bike, I knew my tolerance levels – most of the time – and I was too much of a coward to contemplate killing myself. Paul was different. At thirty-eight, he was the first of my friends to die of old age.

'He did smoke quite heavily, I suppose,' I ventured, searching for some reason why he might have croaked that didn't apply to me.

'And he did do a fair amount of drugs,' said Alex, clearly not bothered about the implications for himself.

'Yeah, and so do you.'

I didn't think Paul's death necessarily precluded spreading a bit of paranoia.

'Oh, bollocks. You know I don't,' he said nastily, though not nearly as convincingly as he tried to sound. A result.

'Well, you do take more than anyone else I know, except. . .' I deliberately left Paul's name hanging in the air.

'You're so boring sometimes. Just because you don't take anything, you reckon that anyone who smokes the odd joint has a problem.'

We were back on familiar territory now. Which was a big relief, because at least we knew where we were when we were winding each other up. Paul's death was simply too much for either of us to deal with right then. It resonated further than the mere death of a friend. It reached deep into our own mortality. Much as we wanted to blame the smoking, the drugs or whatever, we could only do so half-heartedly. Whichever way you looked at it, Paul's death hadn't been caused by one major trauma. There were thousands, perhaps millions, of people still living who had been far more excessive than him. It was just that his body had decided it had had enough and stopped working.

Paul's death made me acutely aware of my own body. I became used to the sound of my heart beating. I would take my pulse regularly and be alert to any arrhythmia. I would sense my chest tightening and would experience strange shooting pains down my left arm. To be frank, I had the odd heart attack.

I also became deeply superstitious. I couldn't go anywhere in the morning before I had read the death notices in the paper. I even went so far as to order the *Telegraph* , as it was the paper with the longest listings. I would start at the 'A's and work my way through, checking the ages of everyone who had died. The more eighties and nineties there were the better, but the real test was whether there was anyone who was younger than me. You couldn't always tell, mind, because some relatives don't bother to include the age. I ask you. Fancy omitting the one crucial piece of info. With these, you could sometimes make an informed guess. If they said 'dearly beloved grandmother or grandfather' I generally assumed they were much older than me. But if it just said 'after a long illness' or 'loving father' you were completely stumped. I had to just put those down as Don't Knows. Likewise I discounted anyone younger than me who had the words 'tragically' in their notice, because I reckoned they had had a nasty accident of some sort. But that still left a number of bods like Paul from time to time. And whenever they appeared I knew I was in for a bad day.

And on these days I would spend hours thinking about Paul. How inevitable was his death? Would a change of lifestyle have made the slightest difference? Not surprisingly, I soon began to question my relationship with doctors. Perhaps 'relationship' is putting it a little strong. The only contact that I'd ever had with my doctor over the previous ten years had been the occasional fleeting five minutes in the surgery. Which should have alerted me. The doctor invariably ran about forty-five minutes late and yet I was only ever in for half my allotted time. Clearly, neither of us was taking my health nearly seriously enough. Our assignations would generally go a bit like this:

'What seems to be the matter. . . ?' Quick glance at my notes. 'John,' she said triumphantly.

'I've got this cough which won't shift.'

'Oh dear. Slip your sweater off and I'll have a listen. Mmm. You are a bit chesty.'

Tell me something I don't know.

'Yeah,' I said meekly.

'Some antibiotics should do the trick. But come back and see me if you're not better in a week.'

And I would actually leave feeling well satisfied. What a great doctor, I would think. But after Paul died, I realized that I was being hopelessly complacent. My doctor obviously didn't really know what was going on with me. She hadn't X-rayed my chest or had my sputum analysed. She had made only a cursory examination and then opted for a best-guess scenario, covering himself with the 'come back next week' leitmotiv which she probably used on all patients.

Luckily for her – and for me, I might add – she got away with it every time. My cough did respond to the antibiotics. But what if it hadn't? What if I'd been suffering from something terminal and he'd missed it? I could have died in the intervening week or have passed the critical point where I failed to respond to treatment. And then what? The doc gets to say, 'I screwed up' and I get to say, 'Bye-bye.' If I'm lucky.

No, the more I thought about it, the more I realized how little I could depend on others for my health. No one was going to take my ailments seriously if I didn't, and the only way to guarantee my survival for as long as possible was to regard any symptom as potentially life-threatening.

As you can imagine, this generated a piss-poor response at home.

'I've got a really bad headache.'

'How come you've always got a headache when it's the kids' bath time?'

I can't tell you what it's like to have a loving, sympathetic partner. Because I just don't know.

'I don't always have a headache at the kids' bath time.'

I wasn't really up to a full-blown argument, but I knew if I didn't stamp on this myth immediately it would become a fact by default.

'I mean, why do you only ever mention you've got a headache at the kids' bath time?' my wife persisted.

'Because I only ever bother you about a headache if it's gone on for more than a few hours. And as they usually start in the afternoon, it's about now that I start getting concerned. The bath time is just a coincidence.'

'Oh, really? I suppose I should be grateful that you've been so stoic all afternoon, then?'

My thoughts precisely.

'I'm just a bit worried, that's all,' I said, trying to be conciliatory and reasonable.

'I'm sorry I snapped,' she said, responding to my charm offensive. 'I'm just knackered. Anyway, what are you worried about?'

'I think I've got a brain tumour.'

'Oh, don't be so fucking ridiculous.' Compassion can be very short-lived sometimes. 'You've just got a headache. Everyone gets them. Besides, you don't have any of the symptoms of a brain tumour.'

'I do. I've got a persistent headache.'

'You haven't. Your headache has only been going on for a few hours.'

'That's persistent.'

'No it's not.'

'Well, it could be. Even persistent headaches have to start somewhere.'

'Oh, for God's sake. You don't have a sodding brain tumour. You'd be flat out and vomiting if you did.'

'Maybe those symptoms haven't cut in yet.'

'Oh, shut up and help me bath the kids. You're just being a complete hypochondriac.'

Hypochondriac? How misunderstood can you get? Hypochondria is the unrealistic and irrational fear of illness – I've just looked it up to check. But there was nothing irrational about my fears. As far as I was concerned, my response was entirely logical. By maintaining extreme vigilance on all things medical, I would be able to pick up anything nasty as soon as it appeared. No unpleasant little cancers were going to get past my early-warning systems, and if it meant confusing the odd headache with a brain tumour, then it was a price well worth paying.

This sort of positive, go-getting action could work for all sorts of things. Like smoking. Sort of. If you think about it rationally, there has to be one cigarette that proves critical. The one that tips you over the edge from being non-cancerous to cancerous. So the trick is to know exactly which one that is going to be and to quit just before you get to it. I can't believe that the tobacco companies haven't latched on to this. Instead of squandering billions on the futile task of trying to prove nicotine non-addictive, they would be far better off developing a machine which could show people when they were going to get lung cancer.

But I quickly realized that people – namely, my wife and friends – were totally unresponsive to original thinking. They much preferred a world where you continued to act as though everything was going to be hunky-dory for ever and ever and illness always came along as a real surprise. Which is daft. Because there are so many germs, so many viruses, so many poisons to clog your arteries, so many cells dying to malignantly mutate, that the only mystery is why we all haven't died a great deal earlier.

For me, though, there was no turning back. And if that meant doing things on my own, then so be it. Naturally, my first investment was in *Black's Medical Dictionary* and *The Reader's Digest Encyclopedia of Family Health*. What fascinating and vital reading they turned out to be.

'Cor. Listen to this,' I said, as I lay in bed reading.

'What is it?' replied my wife, disinterestedly, her head buried in a Joanna Trollope. She'd finished the Jackie Collins.

'Ebola fever. You become delirious, your internal organs liquefy and you start bleeding out of every orifice.'

'Well, you've probably got it then,' she said with a yawn.

'Why do you say that?' I replied, alarmed. Last thing at

night I only ever read those entries that I did think I had a cat in hell's chance of having, otherwise I couldn't get to sleep.

'You're certainly delirious,' she continued.

'Do you think so?'

'Undoubtedly.'

It sank in.

'God. You might be right.'

'You haven't. . .'

'But I had a. . .'

'Got. . .'

'Nosebleed. . .'

'Ebola. . .'

'The other day.'

'Fever.'

'How do you know?'

'Because you haven't been to Zaïre. Not recently. Not ever. I'm going to sleep. Goodnight.'

And with that she turned the light out.

I tried to get to sleep. I really did. But it's hard when something's niggling you. So after ten minutes I whispered, 'Sweetie?'

'What is it now?' she sighed melodramatically.

'Are you really, really sure. . .?'

'Christ. I hate you sometimes. You've made me so angry I can't sleep.'

'That's bad.'

'What's bad?'

'Insomnia and anger are classic symptoms of some particularly virulent diseases.'

No prizes for guessing that my reference books were banned from the bedroom after that waspish little interchange. Which was a major drag, as it meant that I frequently had to go downstairs at 3 a.m. to check a few details. Even this was too much for my wife, though, as she claimed that all my hopping in and out of bed was waking her up. Next thing I knew, both books were missing.

'Have you seen my books?' I asked that night.

'No,' she said sweetly.

Big mistake, my dear. You should have said, 'What books?'

'Are you sure?'

'Positive.'

Well, I was positive too. Positive that she'd given them away or chucked them out somewhere. But I couldn't prove it. She still hasn't worked out why her passport went missing the night before she was about to bugger off to Italy on business, though.

I can be quite tenacious at times. Irritatingly so, some might say. So I wasn't going to let the disappearance of the books interrupt my round-the-clock health watch. If the books weren't going to come to Muhammad, then Muhammad would have to go to the books. WH Smith soon became a regular haunt. It had a surprisingly good medical section and was only a couple of minutes from home. The only major problem I faced was that I got so agitated reading up on the possible causes of my different conditions that I had frequently forgotten the precise wording of the text by the time I got back home. So I was never wholly sure what I did have and what I didn't, and it was too embarrassing to go back to Smith's more than a couple of times a day to find out.

Invariably, though, any prolonged health anxiety – one lasting over twenty-four hours – would be met with a testy 'Why don't you go to the doctor instead of bothering me?' from my wife. I'll tell you why. Because it's dead scary going to the surgery. Think about it. If you trot off to the doc's thinking you've got a minor chest infection and that all you need is a few pills to see you OK, then there's nothing much to it. But when you go along convinced you've got lung cancer, then it's a whole new ball game. You're entering a zone where anything can happen; you might be classified terminal or you might be whisked off for open-heart surgery. This makes it thoroughly nerve-racking, not to mention time-consuming, as you have to make sure there will be someone at home to look after the kids in case you don't come back.

You also want to mark your departure with a certain dignity. You want to look around and absorb the atmos-phere of your home – especially the minor things that you normally take for granted, such as the bloodstains on the wall where Jo pushed Tom down the stairs. It's the good-byes that are the most difficult. I've always felt the need to say something significant. I want to let everyone know how much they mean to me and how much I appreciate all they've done for me – even though it hasn't been nearly as much as I'd have hoped, frankly. But you're expected to lie in this sort of situation. However, by the time I've stumbled across the *mots justes*, the rest of the family has usually pissed off out the front door without so much as a 'See you later'. There again, perhaps they're not so sure that they will.

There's another problem with going to see the quack, of course. For people who have supposedly chosen to enter one of the caring professions, doctors can be remarkably intolerant at times. Oh, they're OK for the first couple of visits. They even smile quite indulgently when you start talking about waiting times on transplant lists. But by the third or fourth occasion, their manner becomes curt and frosty and all that escapes their narrowing lips is 'No, I don't think any further tests are called for.' Mind you, you can predict when the doctor is going to round on you by the reaction you get from the receptionist when you make the appointment.

'Hello, it's. . .'

'I know who it is, Mr Crace. What can I do for you?'

'I'd like to see the doctor, please.'

'The earliest appointment we've got is Tuesday next week.'

'Oh. You don't have anything sooner?'

'No.'

'I'm not sure I can wait that long.'

A long sigh and a muttered 'bloody fat files' is usually audible down the line at this point.

'Is it an emergency then?'

'I'd say so.'

'Are you sure?'

'As sure as I can be.'

'The doctor doesn't like time-wasters, you know.'

'I can understand that. Neither do I.'

'He is very busy.'

'So am I.'

Two can play silly buggers.

'You're saying it's an emergency then?'

'Yeah.'

'So what's wrong with you?'

'I dunno. That's why I need to see the doctor.'

'What do you think might be wrong with you?'

'Leukaemia.'

'I see. Do you think that's very likely?'

'It could be. But it's not something you want to take any chances with, is it?'

Long pause.

'She could fit you in at 11.30 at the end of surgery, I suppose.'

'Tha—'

Click.

It's like getting blood out of a stone. The receptionist could have just said, 'Will 11.30 do?' to my first – very simple – request for an appointment. But no. She insisted on being obstructive and offensive with it. Some people don't have any manners at all.

Anyway, once you're into verbal exchanges like this, your relationship with your doctor is well and truly fucked. You're in a no-win situation. You're dead in the water. Literally, possibly. You see, medics generally work from your case notes. They see you've complained of a number of terminal illnesses that have fortunately turned out to be relatively minor – OK, extremely minor – and when you come along with another suspected disaster they assume there's going to be nothing really wrong. This is criminal negligence. A few narrow escapes in the past have no bearing whatsoever on the future. Hypochondriacs are just as likely to get a real terminal illness as anyone else. We're all going to die of something. It's just that people like me assume it's going to happen sooner and so-called normal people assume it's going to happen later. And it's me that gets labelled bonkers. There's something wrong with that, I think.

So if you're not going to get proper treatment from your GP, where do you go? You can try switching doctors in the hope of finding someone with more insight, experience and – dare one say it? – more than the bare minimum of qualifications, but this is a bit of a long shot. Doctors the world over moan about how difficult their jobs are, what long hours they work, how undervalued they feel etc, etc. How self-pitying can you get? Do they really imagine that everyone else is told how wonderful they are the whole time? In any case, it's not as if the job description has changed radically since they went to medical school, so it can hardly have come as a major shock.

No. Switching doctors is out of the question and adopting disguises and aliases is far too confusing, especially as you're likely to be very ill when you have to do it. The only real solution is to go privately.

Private medicine? That's heresy. That's expensive. Isn't it?

Well, no, it isn't really. First off, going privately is a very New Labour thing to do. Tony Blair wants people like you and me to go privately. It's one of his new very good ideas that he got from the Conservatives. So just do it. Make Tony happy. Ask not what your country can do for you but what you can do for your country.

And getting private health insurance can be really quite cheap. Especially if there's nothing really wrong with you in the first place to load the premiums. The point is that most people use their health insurance extremely stupidly. They look on it as something to fall back on in case they get ill. Thick or what? The trick is to view it as you would membership of a gym. If you only go once a month it's incredibly pricey, but if you go every day then it's a complete bargain. So once you've got your health insurance, go out there and make the most of it.

Private medicine makes being ill even more of a pleasure than it already is. My first encounter seduced me for ever. I'd got the number of a good doctor from a friend who was up on docs, and rang to make an appointment.

'Er, hello. My name is John Crace. I haven't been to the surgery before, but I'd like to see Dr Wilson, please.'

'Certainly, Mr Crace. When would you like to come along?'

'This morning sometime.'

'Would 10.30 or 11.30 suit you?'

You mean I've got a choice?

'Ten-thirty will do just fine.'

'Ten-thirty it is. We'll look forward to seeing you then. And thanks for calling.'

Just listen to that. The doctor wasn't just looking forward to seeing me; he was outright grateful that I was going to make the effort to haul my disease-riddled body over to his surgery. This was much more like it. I felt so much better already.

The feel-good factor went into overdrive when I got to his consulting rooms – as surgeries are called in fashionable parts of central London. Dr Wilson raced out into the waiting-room – on time – to come and get me, shook my hand and led me off to his lair. And after sitting me down and going through my medical history, he looked up.

'How can I help?' he said.

'Umm. Well, I've had diarrhoea for a few days and I'm worried I've got bowel cancer.'

Doc Wilson didn't bat an eyelid. The man was a saint. Or a god. Or something.

'Well, that's not very nice. Let's take a look.'

And by look, I mean look. Out came the latex gloves and up went the finger, along with other indelicate surgical appliances.

'I can't see anything untoward up there,' he said reassuringly. 'Still, best to make sure.'

He reached for his trolley, grabbed a spike, jabbed it in my arm and proceeded to take several kegs full of blood.

'We'll do a full blood screen, I think. And while we're about it we'll take urine and stool samples for analysis,' he said, handing me a couple of receptacles and shepherding me off to his well-appointed lav.

On my return he wrapped a band around my arm and took my blood pressure, popped a thermometer into my mouth, and finally – just for the hell of it, presumably – tested my reflexes.

'That should do it,' he said. 'Anyway, everything is perfectly normal so far. I think you've got a bit of a tummy bug, but the tests should tell us a bit more. I'll ring you tomorrow when the results come through. And honestly, don't give bowel cancer another thought.'

Some hope.

I left the surgery feeling vaguely euphoric. At last I had found a doctor who was prepared to take my health as seriously as me. Not for him any wait-and-see bollocks. He was straight in there, blitzing my body with tests. If I had anything wrong with me – even if it was only what other docs condescendingly referred to as 'an upset' – it was going to be dragged out into the open and named and shamed. But by the time I got to my car I started to have a few doubts. Even it was all being paid for by the insurance, doctors didn't behave like this, did they? Surely they didn't give you a whole load of tests unless they thought there was a chance something sinister was going down.

Back home, my decline deepened.

'Where have you been?' asked my wife aggressively.

It's a fantastic feeling to know you're always at the forefront of your partner's thoughts.

'The doctor's.'

'So you have,' she said, without a hint of contrition. 'Mmm, and . . .'

Go on. Break the habit of a lifetime. Ask me how I am.

'And did you remember to pick up the milk on the way home?'

That's typical of her. Me, me, me, me, me, me. Well, she is half-American. I mean, milk. Is there anything worse to give a bloke with a dodgy tummy than milk? It was just plain sadism that made her ask that.

'No, I didn't actually. I felt too ill.'

'That's odd, since there's nothing wrong with you.'

'Then why have I been to the doctor's?'

'You tell me.'

'Because I might have bowel cancer.'

'But you don't have bowel cancer.'

'That's not what Dr Wilson says.'

A small exaggeration, I admit.

'What?'

A note of concern or just worry that life was about to become inconvenient for her? It was hard to tell.

'Yeah. He's testing me for it.'

Among other things.

'Are you sure?'

'Absolutely. I get the results tomorrow.'

'Oh. Well, it must be just precautionary. You'll be fine.'

Thanks. Don't you just love it when people are so cavalier with your life? It's like saying, 'Don't worry, you'll find something else. Things always work out in the end' to someone who's just lost their job. Because you don't have to look very far to see that things don't always work out. In fact, they often get considerably worse. But no one ever wants to know that. Including my wife. So I am expected to live in a world where my bowel cancer flies into spontaneous remission just to make her feel better.

The twenty-four hours waiting for the results to come through were no breeze. I paced around, I couldn't concentrate on my work and anyone who phoned got bundled off the line sharpish in case the doc was trying to get through. It was before the days of call waiting, which in any case I still haven't entirely mastered. Someone always seems to get cut off. Answers on a postcard, please. But that's by the by.

Unlike drug dealers and ex-girlfriends, Doc Wilson proved to be as good as his word and phoned when he said he would.

'Is that you, John?' he boomed avuncularly.

'Yes.'

C'mon, c'mon. Gimme, gimme.

'Your results look fine. Stool normal, urine normal, liver functions normal. There's just your erythrocyte sedimentation levels, which are up a bit.'

It was great that he felt he could talk dirty to me, but I hadn't a clue what he was on about.

'What are these erythr . . . ?'

'Erythrocytes. Red blood corpuscles. The test shows whether you've been in contact with a virus. You have and it's almost certainly your stomach bug. So, since the rest of your results are normal, you're in the clear. But if your diarrhoea hasn't cleared up in a week or so, don't hesitate to come and see me again.'

'Thanks, I will.'

This was the best result possible. I wasn't going to die, but there was something genuinely the matter with me. Since my wife was her usual disinterested self, it was up to me to let her know the good news.

'The doc rang. My erythrocyte sedimentation levels are up.'

'Oh really,' she said, bored out of her mind. 'What does that mean?'

'It means that bowel cancer can't be entirely ruled out.'

I didn't say this just out of spite. Well, not entirely. She did need to be kept on her toes, but I did also sort of believe it. How accurate were these tests? Could they pick up an early cancer? There was only one thing that was going to settle the issue. Would my diarrhoea get better?

So began a week of intense faecal monitoring. Not a pleasant task, but a necessary one, I'm sure you'll agree. And though there were some signs of improvement there weren't enough to say categorically that I'd made a full recovery. So it was back to you know where.

'I'm still a bit concerned. . .'

'We have done a full set of tests. . .'

'. . .about the bowel cancer.'

'Everything contraindicates it, John,' Dr Wilson said patiently. 'I'd stake my reputation on that you haven't got it.'

But not my life.

'Can you say I'm 100 per cent in the clear then?'

'No. No doctor could. Only a barium enema could determine that.'

I raised an eyebrow.

'Are you sure that's what you want?' he said at length. 'It's not a very comfortable procedure, and it's not what I would ordinarily recommend for you.'

'I understand that.'

'OK then. If it's going to nail this worry once and for all, let's do it.'

Naturally, I didn't tell my wife that I'd had to plead for the barium enema, and even she was a bit impressed that I needed such radical treatment – though she did her best not to let it show.

After two hard days on the laxatives – an essential part of the masochistic build-up to the enema – I found myself dolled up in a fetching light-blue paper dress, lying on an operating table, surrounded by monitors and adjacent to a bag of white gunge, suspended from a hook, which was connected to a plastic hose, the other end of which a nurse was trying to shove up my bum. Horny, it wasn't.

But once I was plugged in, it wasn't that bad either. It felt a bit odd being moved around, feeling the liquid move along my lower intestine, but it also felt good to know that within minutes I would know exactly where I was – apropos bowel cancer. I scanned the screens avidly, but though I could see the outline of my gut I couldn't tell which bits were stuffed with carcinomas and which bits were in good shape. In the end I gave up guessing and switched my gaze to the radiographer. Was she smiling or was she frowning? The answer was neither. I reckon that she must have learnt to give as little away as possible. Either that or she just loved the feeling of power.

The last of the solution squelched out back down the tube, and I was shunted back to the changing room to get dressed. As I was on my way out, the radiographer passed by.

'I haven't done the full report yet, but everything seems absolutely clear,' she said.

It's hard to describe how I felt. Only those who have lived under a similar death sentence can possibly appreciate the relief. In a nanosecond I had gone from being a man with a past to a man with a future. Whole new vistas of TV viewing opened up, as I had abandoned any serials that had more than two episodes on the grounds that it would be too upsetting to miss the end.

Better still, I felt well. I knew my diarrhoea was going to get better. And I looked at other people in the street in a completely different way. How many of them could put their hand on their heart and say that they knew they didn't have bowel cancer? They might not have any symptoms yet, but at that very moment the first cancerous cell division might be taking place. Whereas I knew – had hard, documentary proof – that my intestines were in perfect working order. That's quite something, when you think about it.

Unfortunately, such knowledge dates fairly quickly.

TEN

I know what you're thinking. This bloke's got real problems. He needs help. Don't feel guilty about it, though. You won't upset me. People have been saying things like that for years. In fact, for almost exactly as long as I've been in therapy.

Which is a bit of a worry in itself. Then maybe I'd have been a whole lot worse if I had never been in therapy. You never can tell. But that's one of the things about therapy. You never know anything for sure. Ever. You make a few wild guesses about this and that, accuse a few people you don't like of abusing you as a child and it doesn't really matter whether you're right or wrong, because nobody's any the wiser. Especially you.

What matters, of course, is how you feel. And we're

not talking better or worse here, because those terms are highly judgemental and hence very untherapeutic. In any case, could you ever be certain that you definitely were feeling better? You might think you were, but it could be just a symptom that you were actually getting worse. That's denial for you. Ask my wife. She knows all about that. No, the aim of therapy is simply to get you to feel - the more intensely the merrier. Because then you're in touch with yourself. And very, very deep, sensitive and lovable with it. Just look at me. You might witter on in your sessions about making important changes in your life – who knows, you might even make them – but if you do they are likely to be completely accidental. Which is not to say that your therapist won't try to take all the credit.

I should charge for this sort of information. I really should. Come to think of it, I am. So forget that bit. This is the stuff that nobody tells you about therapy before you start, and you only find out when you're hopelessly locked into an incomprehensible relationship and you can't possibly leave.

Mind you, I'm not sure that it would have made much difference to me even if I had known, as I never went into therapy to get my problems sorted in the first place. For the simple reason that I didn't think I had any problems worth talking about. I went into therapy because it's what all my mates were doing and I didn't want to feel left out. Which can happen very quickly once people start going to therapy as they begin to talk another language.

'I really need to confront you about something, John,' said Dan.

'What?'

'I said I really need to confront you.'

'You mean you want to have a chat?' I guessed. Or have you forgotten what a chat is?

'I mean, I'm finding you hard to deal with.'

What can you say to that?

'Oh.'

'Yeah, I find you really needy.'

'Oh.'

'Don't get me wrong, I'm not blaming you for it. It's mainly my stuff. You just bring up a lot of childhood issues for me and I need some space.'

I'm still not entirely sure what Dan was on about. But aside from the confusion, I can remember feeling incredibly envious. It seems daft now, but I wanted to go around saying that sort of thing to people. It sounded meaningful and portentous, but most of all it seemed to have a magical effect on women.

This was the tail-end of the eighties. No one I knew had managed to hang on to any of the money they were supposed to have made in the Thatcher boom years, and most were struggling even to hold on to their jobs. Things were out and feelings were in. It was pointless having a nice car unless you felt embarrassed or ashamed of it, because people – women, let's be specific – were only going to love you if you had lots of feelings. Preferably bad ones. And at the time I only had two. All right and not so all right.

It was the dawning of the age of male emotional articulacy, and even though I could only ever understand about one word in three of any pronouncement Dan made, he was the arch-exponent. He was the pioneer. He was the first bloke I knew to go into therapy, and women adored him for it.

'How are you feeling, Dan?' they would coo.

'A little bit of pain, a little bit of anger,' he would squeeze out soulfully.

At which point all the women would swoon in a collective orgasm of identification, and you just knew that Dan would be able to take his pick of which one he was going to get off with.

Needless to say, by the time I learnt to be fluent in psychobabble the rules of the game had changed somewhat. You needed to have been in therapy for at least a year before a woman would take you seriously. But that's the story of my life. Always hopelessly behind the times.

But I didn't know that then. So you could say that therapy has taught me one thing. Besides, no one ever, ever, ever talked about therapy as making you attractive to others. Therapy was serious stuff. It was personal development. It was a journey into the unknown. And mine was about to begin.

'I'm planning on going into therapy,' I said to my wife one night over supper.

Well, it was only polite to let her know what I was up

to. Would that such social niceties ever got reciprocated, though. I usually only get to hear of her plans from her friends.

'Really?' she replied, stifling a yawn. 'Why?'

Christ, what was this? No one's meant to ask that question. Therapy is something that one just goes into. It doesn't require any explanation. And as if I was going to tell her it was because Dan, Ben and Ashley were.

'Because I want to heal my child within.'

Sometimes my genius amazes me. There I was, put on the spot, and it just came to me. Thank you, Dan.

Or maybe not.

'You do talk some pretentious crap sometimes,' she said. 'Besides, your problem isn't the child within – it's the bloody child without.'

'Oh, ha, ha,' I riposted as sarkily as possible. Which wasn't very, as I'm never at my best when I'm being taken to the cleaners.

'Why don't you just admit that it's because you want to be like Dan, Tom and Ashley?'

'Because it's not true,' I said, looking for a way out of this little dead end. 'Sure, they might have opened my eyes to the possibility. But I'm going for my own reasons.'

'Which are to make yourself more attractive to women, I suppose?'

'Don't be so ridi. . .'

'Don't worry, it's fine by me,' she said with a cackle. 'You need all the help you can get.'

'Oh, thanks.'

'Well, you are getting on a bit.'

'I'm not.'

I am.

'Oh, come on. Relax,' she said, with a sudden influx of charm. 'I was only taking the piss. Look, I'm sure therapy will do you some good. After all, it can hardly make you any worse.'

I think she probably regrets that remark now.

'That's hardly a ringing endorsement.'

'But it's not a bad downside. Besides, apart from talking more twaddle than usual, Dan, Tom and Ashley still seem reasonably normal.'

'So you don't mind then? You don't need some time to think about it?'

Hey. Who needs therapy when you can come up with stuff like that?

'Nah. It's fine by me.'

'Sure?'

'Yeah. I knew all about it anyway. Debby told me you'd been talking to Ben about going into therapy last week.'

It's one thing to decide you're ready for therapy, and quite another to actually find a shrink. It's meant to be easy, of course. You're meant to natter to other people in therapy and take up their personal recommendations. Only it never worked out like that. No one I knew wanted to share their therapist with anyone else they knew. So they were only prepared to recommend someone they weren't in therapy with. Which meant I would be palmed off with second-best – if I was very lucky. Because you couldn't be sure that the therapist in question hadn't offered bounty money to anyone who managed to round up a few unsuspecting punters. I certainly wouldn't have put it past any of my friends.

And that was just the start of it. Any therapist worth seeing isn't going to be able to see you anyway. Unless you're very, very famous. And then they're mysteriously open all hours. Di, Fergie, Elton, Liz. You don't think they had to wait, do you? Oh no. It's 'Do come round. Of course it doesn't matter that it's three in the morning.' But for the rest of us, it's 'I'm sorry I don't have a vacancy at the moment. Leave me your number, and I'll give you a call in three or four months to let you know if anything crops up.' Gee, thanks. I feel so much better for your support. I don't think I'll kill myself after all.

So when you do find someone who can see you, you automatically assume they can't be any good. And sometimes you'll be right.

It's a terrible thing to admit, but I can't remember the name of my first therapist. I remember the road, I remember the building, I remember the room, but I can't remember her. Not what she looked like nor what she was called. And I'm certain that I made a similar impression on her, as throughout our brief relationship she never showed much interest in anything I said.

Naively, I took this to be a sign of her professionalism. I would drone on and on about how my mum had done this and my dad had done that, and she would stare blankly back, with only the occasional 'Uh, huh', 'Go on' or 'How did that feel?' to punctuate her silence. The only time she ever got animated was when she looked at her watch, leapt to her feet and rushed to open the door with a celebratory 'Same time next week'.

And troop back I would, in the belief that I was going through something profound. This is where it helps to be paying through the nose. OK, it was only £20 a session back then – chicken-feed by today's tariffs – but £20 is still £20. And when you're forking it out week in, week out you need to think that it's doing you the world of good. Still, at least one of us was making me feel the whole process was worthwhile.

We reached the nadir after about two months, when I pressed her buzzer a few times, hung around outside the mansion block for about ten minutes and then buggered off home again. I suppose that under normal circumstances you might have expected me to ring her or her to ring me to find out what had happened. But neither of us bothered. We just weren't that close, I guess.

So I just carried on as normal till the following week. By which time I was feeling very angry. But very excited, too. I had my first real therapy issue to confront.

'So where were you last week?' I opened aggressively.

'And where were you?' she replied evenly.

This was the nearest we had ever got to normal dialogue. It felt disconcertingly intimate.

'I was here, but you weren't. I rang your buzzer for ages.'

'Well, I was here too. And I never heard you ring.'

'Perhaps your buzzer was broken?'

'It wasn't. I checked.'

'So what happened then?'

'You tell me.'

She obviously had as much trouble dealing with Paul McKenna's *World of the Paranormal* as I did.

'Well, I definitely pressed the buzzer.'

'Are you sure?'

'Are you suggesting that I subconsciously didn't want to come to my session and that I pressed the wrong buzzer or something?'

'I'm not saying that. But you are. Would you like to talk about it?'

She was clearly a great deal cleverer than I had given her credit for. With little more than a few verbal shimmies she had laid the blame fair and square at my feet, even though what had clearly happened was that she had nodded off in her armchair ten minutes earlier than she usually did and had slept through the bell.

Despite this unexpected show of intelligence on her part, things never really picked up after that. We plodded on for a few more sessions, during which I moaned a bit about this and that and brought her up to date with my emotional history, until she suddenly interrupted me.

'We've done some fantastic work together,' she said. 'You've made great progress.'

Glad she thought so. But it was news to me. I didn't feel I'd ever got started.

'Really?' I said, flattered nonetheless.

'Oh, yes. I think we've gone as far as we can on a one-to-one basis. It might be helpful, though, to see you and your wife together. As a couple. How would you feel about that?'

'Erm. Seems OK to me. But I'm not sure how my wife will feel about it. Maybe you should check it out with her first.'

'Of course. So you wouldn't mind if I phoned her to discuss it?'

'Not at all.'

I hasten to add that this is not the kind of thing anyone should agree to. Letting your partner anywhere near your therapist is asking for big, big trouble. They should be kept as far apart as possible. You never know what they might get up to together. They might even like each other – more than either of them likes you. But I didn't know any better back then. Fortunately, there were no serious repercussions. Because predictably, my therapist never got round to phoning my wife. And I never got round to phoning her to ask why not. So that was the end of my first foray into being shrunk. No tears, no goodbyes, just a fading away with a complete lack of thought and respect on both sides. Like the ending of so many of my relationships really.

But once bitten, definitely not twice shy. If anything, I was keener than ever to get theraped, because – apart from the cash – the experience had cost me next to nothing. The only real feeling I'd been made to have was anger over not being let in, while for the rest of the time I'd been able to hold court on my favourite subject – me – without any emotional comeback. If only it had stayed that way.

For some reason it wasn't nearly so tricky finding a shrink second time round. I suppose it's a bit like getting a job. Every employer wants previous experience but no one's ever prepared to give it. Or maybe it was just my track record of paying on time that made me suddenly so irresistible. Either way, I was given the number of a woman in north London, by someone whom I trusted – yes, a bona fide recommendation, I had made it in the industry – and after a quick phone call I was back in business.

I don't have any problem remembering what this therapist was called or what she looked like. But then you'd have to have some degenerative brain disorder not to recognize someone you saw regularly for nearly eight years. Her name was Mary, a prim, middle-classish sort of name, which almost perfectly matched her physical description. She was neither fat nor thin, short nor tall, good-looking nor ugly, young nor old – she was just, well, averagely nondescript. And if that sounds excessively damning, it's not meant to be. Excessive, that is. Because in many ways Mary was the perfect physical embodiment of a therapist – a *tabula rasa* on which any number of different fantasies could be projected.

But her voice was something else all together. You know how some people's voices you can hear in your head as if they were speaking to you? Well, Mary's wasn't one of those, even though it should have been. Because it was one of the most distinctive voices I've ever heard. She spoke in the most measured, pedantic monotone you could ever imagine. Whatever was going on in the session, her voice never betrayed a hint of animation or modulation. She had a numbness, a robotic quality, that could have been confused for utter boredom, were it not impossible for someone to be that bored for so long. It was all a bit spooky, not least because whenever I tried to replay it – to re-create her speech – my mind went blank. And even now I don't know if it was down to my mental block or her supernatural powers of erasure.

She lived in a house that had an enormous crack down the outside front wall and was situated at the very end of a cul-de-sac. Funnily enough, these two details were the only ones to escape a symbolic interpretation throughout our relationship. Her consulting room, as she grandiosely called it, was little more than a shed attached to the side of the house, which was painted a sickly shade of lilac, and had a few rugs with Eastern motifs – very Carl Jung, very Habitat – hanging on the walls. None of which I minded much; it wasn't totally offensive, didn't give me an instant headache and provided something to wind her up about when I couldn't think of anything else to say.

No, what got me most about her house was the location. It was stuck out somewhere in the north London wilderness, two stops from the end of the tube line, miles outside the North Circular and above all miles from where I lived in Streatham. At the very least it used to take me an hour and a quarter to get to her for my therapeutic hour – aka fifty minutes – and another hour and a quarter to get home. It would have been far less hassle for someone living in Milton Keynes to get to my shrink than it was for me, and I often wondered whether any good the sessions might have done me was more than offset by the sheer aggro of the journey.

Anyone with any sense would quite obviously have reckoned the whole thing was a non-starter from the word go. They would have said to Mary, 'I'm sure you're a great therapist, but I think I'll look for someone a little closer to home.' But I've never had much sense, didn't have a clue how to go about finding anyone nearer – do they even have therapists in south London? – and in any case if all you're going to do is behave rationally, then there's not much point in being in therapy in the first place. You might just as well chat to a couple of strangers in the park – psychology experiments seem to indicate that this will do you about as much good.

But who wants to talk to a stranger for nothing when you can talk to one for £30, and who wants to wander down the park when you can migrate across London in the rush hour? Not me, apparently. Though that didn't stop me moaning about it. Particularly when the journey took far longer than usual and I was ten minutes late, or £6 late, as I chose to think of it.

'Christ, Mary. This is just a fucking nightmare,' I huffed.

'What's a fucking nightmare?'

It used to feel really odd hearing Mary swear, but whenever I swore she would insist on repeating what I said. I think she felt she was using some sophisticated mirroring technique; I reckoned she was just up for any chance to talk dirty.

'The journey's a fucking nightmare. I've been stuck in traffic ever since Kilburn. Why do you have to live in a dump like this? Why can't you be working out of Hampstead like any other self-respecting shrink?'

'And what does it mean to you that I live where I live?' she replied after a moment's thought.

'It means that you don't really give a toss about me one way or the other or you'd make the effort to move somewhere more convenient and nearer to me.'

'Hmm. Interesting you should say "nearer". Perhaps it's you that has difficulty being close to me?'

'What do you mean?' I said, playing for time, though I had a fair idea of what was coming next.

Sure enough.

'I mean that maybe the reason you were late is that at

some level you didn't want to be here. Didn't want to relate to me.'

'Oh, sure. I arranged the roadworks myself, just so as I could spend less time with you.'

'But if you'd made allowances for delays and left earlier, you would have been on time.'

'I did make allowances. I left at exactly at the same time as I always do and I've never been late before. So does this mean I've actually been trying to be late for my sessions all this time and been failing miserably? Or could it just be that the traffic was worse than could reasonably have been predicted?'

'All I'm saying is that you were late. You've deprived yourself of ten minutes of your session and you're upset about it. And rather than get lost in the practicalities, it's an opportunity to have a look at what it means at a deeper level.'

'Well, if we're talking commitment, how about considering that seeing you takes hours out of my day while you only have to shuffle a few yards from your kitchen and that you're the one trousering £30 for the privilege? So who's putting more effort into the relationship?'

'Now, John,' Mary, said in her best matronly voice, 'I'm not saying you don't care about the relationship. I think it's great that you value yourself enough to make the efforts you do. But being late is a sign of holding something back, and I wouldn't be doing my job properly if I didn't take it up with you.'

'So the only way I can prove I'm not holding anything back is by never being late. So perhaps I ought to allow three hours to get here, just in case my car blows up and there's a simultaneous lightning bus and tube strike. Or perhaps I should just camp in your garden the night before my session.'

'Now you're just being absurd,' she observed tartly.

But at least she had come up with something on which we could both agree, and I decided to let the matter drop. Apart from anything else, it's too harrowing to continue when you're paying to have conversations like this. If I wasn't nuts at the beginning of the session, I certainly was by the end.

And that was the basis on which we proceeded. Maybe I've got it wrong somewhere along the line, but it felt as though everything was equally possible and impossible for Mary. Everything was up for grabs, open to myriad interpretations of her choosing; there were no fixed points to latch on to, except her fees, the time of my sessions and the fact that she was invariably right and I was invariably fucked up. Almost anything I presented to her as an example of something good in my life was slowly but inexorably twisted into a prima facie case of emotional and spiritual squalor. It didn't happen often, but when I did say something like 'I'm rather proud of that article I wrote', the knives would be out.

'Can you hear the arrogance, the contempt in what you're saying?' she would hiss. 'I, I, I, I, I. You're off in a world of your own. You think you've done it all by yourself. All those who have helped you, like me and your editor, are rubbished and forgotten. You're in control and you need nobody.'

'I don't think I am saying that at all,' I would reply. 'I am grateful for the help I've been given. I just thought an Oscar acceptance speech would be out of place here.'

But the damage was done. Although I was grateful, how could I ever be sure I was grateful enough? What was the measure of proper gratitude? I knew I was capable of being an ungrateful, selfish bastard, and was this just another example? Was I so messed up that I was incapable of recognizing what was really what any more? Was I just rewriting my own life like some Stalinist historian? I just couldn't be wholly sure. And each time it happened the chinks would open a little wider. It was a drip-by-drip descent into chaos.

There was no relief to be had. It was no good bouncing into a session, boasting about how foul I'd been to someone, as there were no takers to share in the applause for that.

In some ways it might look as if it was all straightfor-wardly black and white. Anything good I did was down to everyone else, and everything bad was my own fault. But it was never that simple. Because I could never predict how bad anything was going to get. There were infinite layers of badness to be revealed, each more vile than the one before.

Mary's specialist subject was anger. My anger.

'I'm fucking furious,' I would say at the start of a session.

'What about?'

And off I would pootle into a long diatribe against whoever or whatever had done me wrong.

From this you might conclude that my problem was that I was too angry – ready to have a go at anyone at any time. But you would be wrong.

'I don't feel that you're really angry about that,' Mary would say at last.

'Well, what am I pissed off about then?'

'I think you're pissed off with me.'

This was a typically irritating remark, as I always had some low-level annoyance going on with her and so couldn't deny it outright.

'I might be a bit pissed off with you,' I would concede, 'but Terry going behind my back is what's really getting me.'

'I disagree,' Mary would insist.

She could carry on this sort of exchange indefinitely. She had great patience. And the net result was that if I wasn't pissed off with her at the start of the session I was practically ballistic by the end.

'I'm really fucking angry with you now,' I would snarl.

'I knew you were all along.'

This sort of thing became a bit of a pattern. Anything that came up in a session was primarily to do with me and her. I might have been talking about a weird dream, my relationship with my mother or just some inconsequential bullshit about how the garage hadn't finished mending the car when it said it would. It was all the same to Mary. All subjects led back to her and me. Me and her. I sometimes wondered whether she wasn't even more self-obsessed than I was.

Her thrust seemed to be that if only we could get our relationship straight, then somehow all my other relationships in the outside world would fall into place. I'd probably never even have to worry about finding a free parking meter ever again. But getting it right was down to me. Mary was making all the right moves, giving all the right signals; it was just me. Emotionally illiterate old me. Me, who couldn't find the words to say whatever needed to be said to reach a therapeutic nirvana. It was horribly frustrating, as I had no idea what more I could say to her to achieve the necessary honesty. I told her that I hated her. I told her that I loved her. But nothing was good enough.

I cried from time to time, too. And not just a few gentle tears, like you get watching an old weepie. *ET* does that for me every time. No, we're talking violent sobs of desperation. But they got me precisely nowhere, too. Crying isn't all it's cracked up to be – even though it's become one of the benchmarks for male emotional well-being. This is why I've never had time for films like *Secrets and Lies* and *Good Will Hunting*. At the end of *Secrets and Lies* everyone tells each other the truth, has a bit of a shout and a blub, and then they all live happily ever after. Same with *Good Will Hunting*. Boy genius goes into therapy, finally admits he was abused by his dad, breaks down in tears, and then everything's fine and he's off to LA to shag Minnie Driver. All I can say is, 'On yer bike, grasshopper.' Catharsis is a myth that lives in the minds of a few shrinks and a few film directors. In my experience these kinds of miracles just don't happen. Crying gives you a momentary release, but you've still got the same old shit to deal with when you stop.

Bizarrely, though, there seemed to be an inverse relationship between my internal and external worlds. The shittier I felt about myself, the more my life seemed to fall into place. For the first time my work had taken on the shape of something that amounted to a career, and my wife and I had gone on to have two kiddies. Now, it could be argued that these things might have happened anyway, but you never know. So it was hard not to think Mary was doing me some good. I just assumed that feeling lousy was the price of creativity.

'Why do you never have a good feeling about anything?' my wife said one day.

'What's there to feel good about?'

'How about your two healthy kids and a decent job?'

'They're OK, I suppose,' I said guardedly. 'But the kids could be wiped out in a car accident and my career could be derailed any day.'

'Christ, you're so depressing to be with. Yeah, and you could drop down dead yourself.'

You wish.

'That's precisely the sort of thing I'm talking about.'

'Do you have any idea of what it's like to live with someone who never enjoys anything. It's so tiring.'

'But I can't help it.'

'Of course you can. You just don't want to. You like being depressed. Frankly,' she added, warming to her theme, 'I find the whole thing offensive. Is it that bad being married to me?'

There are some questions you have to be very careful how you answer.

'Of course not.'

Arguments like this began to take place quite frequently, though I think the reason had less to do with my own state of mind and more to do with my wife's. Because she felt competent enough to comment on my therapy, one of her close women friends had embarked on her own. Well, she called it therapy. I called it counselling. And there's a big difference. It's the difference between the Premier League and the Vauxhall Conference League. And she was in the Vauxhall Conference. She had found a counsellor who had bamboozled her with a string of qualifications that she took at face value – not realizing that one was a NVQ in social work and the other an accreditation for a driving instructor. This happens more often than you would think. I know of one shrink who insists on being called 'Doctor' even though he got his PhD in botany – and off she went once a week for a gentle ego massage.

Which she enjoyed. She learnt a lot of very useful things about herself. Like she felt so much better about herself if she didn't always leave paying the bills until the electricity company threatened to cut her off. That sort of thing. But neither she nor my wife could get their head round the idea that it was a necessity for me to feel lousy the whole time. Then, in truth, I couldn't quite get my head round it either, but I didn't know what to do. Mary did, though.

'You're having problems holding on to any of the good things I give you,' she said.

I wasn't aware that I was even getting any good things. Having trouble holding on to them would have been a sign of real progress.

'What are you going to do about it then?' I asked.

'What are WE going to do about it, John? Therapy is a two-way process.'

Oh, really?

'I've no fucking idea. I'm stumped.'

'Well, luckily there's one of us in this room who hasn't stopped thinking,' she said rather bitchily. 'And I think that you should increase your sessions to two a week.'

'Why? Are you hard-up?'

'Why do you always try to rob what I say of any meaning?'

'I'm not,' I replied huffily. 'I'm just aware that it's going to cost me an extra thirty notes a week. You might just as well transfer your mortgage over to me and I'll pay it by direct debit.'

'This isn't about the money, is it? An extra £30 is a small price to pay for your emotional well-being.'

'But it isn't you that's going to be paying it. How about a reduction for the second session?'

'It's about your reluctance to get closer to me,' she continued, conveniently ignoring what I'd just said. 'You're frightened of what will happen if you let me see the real you.'

We were back to this one. But I was still going to keep an eye on that crack on her front wall to see how long it would be before the work got started.

'You have seen the real me.'

'I don't think so. I've only seen those bits you've let me. You won't be nearly so in control if you come to see me twice a week.'

'But what if coming twice a week only makes me feel twice as bad?'

'I don't think it will happen.'

'But it will make me a complete weirdo,' I blustered. 'Nobody goes to therapy twice a week without being a complete fuck-up.'

'How do you know?'

'Well, no one else I knows goes twice a week.'

'And that's supposed to be a representative sample?'

'It's a start.'

'Let me tell you that you're wrong. Many, many normal people go to therapy twice a week.'

And Mary couldn't be budged from that position. To

her, going to therapy twice a week was on a par with shopping at Sainsbury's. Routine behaviour. She just couldn't understand that telling most people you went to therapy twice a week was social suicide. She had clearly retreated so far into a world that was populated solely by other therapists, and where all relationships had become meta-relationships – existing only to be talked about – that normality had become warped beyond recognition. Though she always maintained that it was my idea of normality that was warped. Maybe we were both clueless.

Yet there was something perversely attractive about her world, and after a few weeks of feeble resistance I found myself agreeing to doubling my therapy. Mary called it acknowledging the well part of me; I wondered whether I was happy to be bonkers.

'Things will change,' she said confidently.

And they did. True to form, the trappings of my life got better and better, so Mary was right about me not missing the extra £30. Internally, though, my mental disintegration went into free fall.

I didn't help my cause by deciding that I was ready to play therapeutic hardball. No more namby-pamby sitting down in a chair for me. It was the analyst's couch from now on. Or bed, in Mary's case. Which was another bone of contention between us. Mary was adamant that her bed was a couch, while I was equally certain that her bed was a bed. It had four little legs, a base and a mattress covered by some kind of throw with elaborate Eastern designs. I guess it was either the throw or the Eastern patterns that turned her bed into a couch as far as Mary was concerned.

Anyway, Mary was clearly delighted that I had advanced to the bed.

'It's a sign that you're beginning to trust me. The absence of eye contact will allow us much greater access to your unconscious,' she said.

Initially my unconscious proved to be a big disappointment. I had often wondered whether I was a bloke with hidden shallows and my early outings on the couch seemed to confirm this. I found that I was paranoid about what she was up to while I was lying there, as she had very cleverly positioned herself so that she was sitting behind my head, where I couldn't see her. I wasn't worried that she was going to axe me to death – she needed the money too much – but I was anxious that I had given her *carte blanche* to doze off, daydream and generally pay the minimum amount of attention to what I was saying.

But I learnt to live with these concerns – not least because I soon became consumed with more pressing matters. Maybe it was lying on the bed that did it, or maybe we'd just reached that point in the relationship, but I found myself fancying Mary. Which came as a big surprise, but then perhaps you can get around to fancying anyone if you spend enough time with them. It's not unheard of for people to fall in love with their torturers. My first reaction was acute embarrassment. Embarrassment that I had become a living cliché by wanting to shag my shrink, and embarrassment that I was going to have to find the words to say so to her.

'Er. . . Mary,' I stumbled, like a moronic adolescent. 'I've got something quite difficult to say. I think I fancy you. Sexually.'

'I see,' she replied, a little coldly. 'I think that what's happening is that you're expressing your loving feelings through your sexual feelings.'

To give Mary her due, she was probably spot on. But it wasn't terribly helpful. I'd already told her that I loved her in the past. And all that had happened then was that she'd said that she felt I wasn't being wholly honest and that there was more to my loving feelings than I was letting on. Which was her rather dishonest way of saying that she thought I fancied her. But I didn't at the time. Or not so as I had noticed, and it's not something that normally escapes me.

Yet when I did get round to fancying her, I got trashed for it. I couldn't win. Either I said I loved her and was not owning up to my lust, or I said I fancied her and was not owning up to my love. And saying that I loved and fancied her at the same time didn't go down too well either, for some reason. I felt lost. I felt like I was a failure at therapy. Whatever words, whatever language I used, I could make no impact. There was always something wrong. I was constitutionally incapable of getting close to anyone.

'I don't think I'm getting anywhere,' I said one day. 'In fact, I feel like I'm getting worse and worse. Perhaps I'm just a psychopath.'

'Do you know what a psychopath is?'

Yes. You.

'Yes.'

'Well, you should know that you're not one. But you are a man with a lot of problems. I think you need more help.' I didn't need to be a psychic to guess what was coming next. 'I think you need another session per week.'

'Christ, where's it going to stop? How long will it be before I'm coming four or five days a week? Maybe you're just no good. Have you ever thought about that?'

Not for a second, it seemed.

'We're not talking about four or five sessions a week. I'm suggesting three, because that's what I think you need.'

And so, like a dependent child, off I went three times a week. I would occasionally ask how long I needed to be in therapy, and would always get the enigmatic reply: 'Therapy has a beginning, a middle and an end' without ever being told my exact location on the continuum. And if I ever dared to suggest leaving or reducing my sessions, I was accused of trying to sabotage all the good work we had done.

Mary knew her stuff, though. I did only need three sessions a week. Not four. Not five. Just three. Three was exactly what it took to drive me completely round the bend.

ELEVEN

One thing I never knew about hypochondria: it can even take a hypochondriac by surprise.

I'd reckoned my condition had got as bad as it could possibly get. No trifling illnesses for me. Nothing easily curable with a few pills and a couple of weeks in bed. Instead I'd confined myself to the nasties; I'd had numerous Aids scares, umpteen carcinomas and a series of heart attacks – any one of which could have proved fatal. Obviously it had been a bit of a drag being this ill – time-consuming, wearing on the personal relationships and so on – but at least I was still alive. I was a survivor.

Idiot.

I was complacent, that's all. My body had just been playing with me. It had been coming up with symptoms that were easily verifiable. One blood test, one X-ray, one biopsy, one MRI scan, one ECG, and I was in the clear. Or not. But even not being in the clear wouldn't necessarily have been a disaster. Protease inhibitors meant that AIDS wasn't a foregone conclusion; a heart transplant or quadruple bypass offered a way out of coronary disease; and even the most vicious of cancers offered a five per cent survival rate after five years. There was always the possibility of a reprieve. Maybe not hopeful; but certainly not hopeless.

But then my body went for the big one; death a cast-iron certainty within twelve months and post-mortem the only definite means of diagnosis. Yup, I had BSE – or new variant Creutzfeldt–Jakob disease, to give it its proper title. I blame the doctors for this. Medical research is always finding new things for you to die of. There we all were, happily noshing our way through the odd dodgy burger, thinking the worst that could happen was a dose of botulism. And then whoosh, along comes some clever dick saying we could all go bonkers and die within a year. Well, thanks for nothing, pal.

Predictably, the first symptoms appeared on Christmas Eve. This may have had something to do with my Christmas allergy, but whatever it was, I started to feel very weird. Look, I know weird isn't that precise a term, but I'm sure anyone with any experience of BSE will know exactly what I'm on about. My head started swimming, nothing seemed real and I felt as if I was about to fall off my chair. Like Bambi on ice.

I tried to compose myself. I really did. I made myself think rationally about what might be going on. Quick mental checklist. Heart attack? No stabbing chest pains. Brain tumour? No headache. It was all very mysterious. So ignoring it was out the question.

The answer came to me at three in the morning, while my symptoms were still raging. BSE. Worry, dislocation, loss of perspective . . . all I needed was the dementia and I had the lot. And as any fool knows, dementia only kicks in towards the end.

The rest of the night passed sleeplessly. I wanted to be conscious for as much of the time I had left as possible. But what a sad, lonely death it was going to be. Not being able to recognize my own children, having my spinal cord and thymus ripped out the moment I snuffed it, and having my body dumped while they tried to clear the backlog of cattle through the incinerator.

My restless shuffling woke my wife at six o'clock. She took one look at me and went for the jugular.

'You're having another illness, aren't you?' she said accusingly.

'No, I'm just thinking, that's all,' I replied.

So far, a normal opening gambit on both sides. It's kind of expected that I shouldn't make too much of a fuss too soon.

'Yes you are. I can see it in your eyes.'

'What? You can tell I've got BSE just by looking at my eyes?'

'You know what?' she said ever so slowly. 'I fucking hate you sometimes. It's Christmas Day, the kids are going to be coming in with their stockings soon, and you're dying of BSE. Is there anything that you can't ruin when you put your mind to it?'

Mmm. No, I doubt it. I've managed to fuck up most things I've turned my hand to.

'Look, I didn't ask to get BSE.'

'You haven't got BSE, you moron.'

Hmm. Moron. Perhaps she thinks the dementia has started after all. But maybe not the best time to press her on this.

'How do you know?'

'Because there's never anything wrong with you'

I wasn't going to be taken in by that line.

'So why do I feel so weird?'

With that she started attacking me, her fists pummelling my body as I curled up to protect myself. I mention this for no other reason than to ensure I get custody of the kids if my wife and I ever split up. Clearly, she is a violent and unstable woman and can't be trusted. And how did I respond to this unprovoked assault? I lay there and took it. Like a man. I didn't hit back. I didn't even threaten her. For truly I am a saint. Just like Bob Geldof. Or perhaps not. But maybe I just misunderstood her. Maybe she thought it was just the thing to cheer me up. So next time I come across a cancer patient with only months to live, remind me to beat the shit out of him.

Somehow I knuckled my way through Christmas and New Year. My symptoms didn't get any worse; neither did they get any better. Which was just what you would expect with BSE. No sudden, dramatic collapse. Just a slow falling apart. So, understandably, my finger was hovering over the telephone the moment the surgery reopened on 2 January.

'Hello, John,' said Dr Wilson, letting me in with far too much festive *joie de vivre* for my liking. 'I was wondering whether you would be my first patient of the new year.'

I told you he was a good doctor. He could intuit when one of his patients was in trouble. My few remaining brain cells had been whizzing through the ether into his consciousness. Which would help to explain why I was going barmy. I was being metaphysically robbed of my sanity.

'Why's that?' I said.

'Um, er, well, it's Christmas and there's a lot of germs about,' he replied awkwardly. 'Anyway, what seems to be the matter this time?'

I didn't like his emphasis on the last two words, but decided to let it go. You've got to let doctors have their little jokes.

'I've got neurological problems.'

'Oh dear. That's not very nice. What sort of neurological problems?'

'I think it's BSE.'

Dr Wilson's eyes closed, and he took a deep breath. He didn't want to look too excited at the thought of treating such a rare case.

'Let's have a look at you then,' he said, before checking out my balance and other brain functions. 'As I suspected, nothing much wrong at all,' he said eventually. 'Your wobbliness is probably down to blocked sinuses.'

I didn't like the sound of 'probably'.

'So it's definitely not BSE then?'

'It's definitely not BSE.'

But how could I trust him? Almost certainly he knew as little about BSE as I did. There'd only been seventeen victims before – I'd checked – working at a newspaper comes in handy sometimes – and in every case it seemed that the doctors had initially tried to pin the symptoms on neurosis. As if.

So reassurance was no reassurance. I was a desperate man. There were no tests, the doctor had done what he could and my wife was trying to assassinate me. Desperate times call for desperate measures. So I asked Mary for help.

'I'm going fucking nuts,' I said simply. 'I can't sleep, I can't work, I'm getting panic attack after panic attack, and I keep bursting into tears. I'm fucking fucked.'

'What do you mean exactly by "fucking fucked"?' she asked.

I mean I've become incoherent. Language has lost its power, its meaning. Every word I think of seems inadequate, too bland, to describe my desperation. I've become like a five-year-old with Tourette's syndrome.

'I mean I'm cracking up. I've had enough. I can't go on. I'm going mad.'

Only it wasn't at all what I had always imagined going mad to be like. I'd just thought it would be like your mind wandering off with the fairies somewhere, thinking you're Napoleon, that sort of thing. Quite nice really. This was different, though. I could actually feel myself slipping away into madness. I was aware of what reality was, but I just couldn't hang on to it. I was sane enough to realize that it was quite possible I didn't have BSE, but not enough to believe it. 'Pull yourself together,' I would say to myself. 'Fucking pull yourself together.' But I couldn't. I just couldn't.

Talking to people was sheer hell generally. Not because I couldn't manage it, but because I could. I would try to explain what I was feeling, but I would only get incomprehension back. I had reached a point of desolation, a place where people I loved could no longer relate to me. I could see the fear in their faces and it scared the shit out of me.

All of which was only of passing interest to Mary, of course, as the only reason I came to see her was so that we could talk about her.

'I think we are beginning to see what happens when you start to get really close to me,' she said. 'You find it so difficult that you would rather die, or imagine that you were dying, than allow yourself to be intimate.'

'I'm not up to this kind of stuff right now. It's all I can do to get through the rest of the day. I just want to be looked after.'

'I am looking after you. But I'm doing it in my way. Not yours. And you can't stand that, can you?'

Now, what do you think?

'Of course I fucking don't.'

'See how quick you are to get angry with me?' she monotoned. 'Anger is another of the ways you deflect any intimacy.'

We went round and round in circles like this for several sessions; she insisting that the answer to my problem lay in the psychodynamics of our relationship, and me insisting that I wasn't up to dealing with such abstract niceties. I think she thought I was just being wilfully obstinate – even more difficult than usual – when I kept asking her to refer me somewhere else. That I couldn't hack it any longer.

'You don't need anyone else,' she would say.

'I just can't seem to get through to you,' I pleaded.

'Oh, but you can. It's me that can't get through to you.'

Finally, after much toing and froing, and with a great show of reluctance, tinged with a desire to show how indulgent and caring she could be, Mary consented to have a word with my GP. And since I knew that all she would tell him was that I was going through a minor therapeutic process, and that Doc Wilson, for all his charm, had little truck with shrinkery, I could see I was going nowhere fast. If I wanted to recover from BSE I was going to have to do it without the pair of them.

This is where it can help to have a thoroughly impatient partner.

'I can't stand much more of this,' my wife said one evening.

'Well, I'm having the time of my life,' I replied, in a rare moment of lucidity.

'Still got a sense of humour, though,' she remarked with surprising sincerity.

Christ. Things must be bad. Up till now my wife had never found my humour anything other than irritating. For her to be pleased at a rather feeble display of wit could only mean one thing. She really did think I might be on the way out.

I immediately felt the onset of another panic attack. My body started shaking uncontrollably, my eyes leaked tears and my breathing went hyper. I dashed upstairs to bed – the only place in the house where I felt remotely safe. Not that I had any idea what bad thing was likely to happen downstairs. I just knew that whatever it was, it wasn't going to happen in bed.

'You're not going to die tonight,' I muttered to myself repeatedly, in an effort to find something positive and calming to focus on. 'But what about tomorrow?' my mind replied. While my brain was busy indulging this internal quarrel, I overheard my wife on the telephone. It wasn't a natter; it was rather more urgent than that. The sort of voice she uses to fire people, I expect. The distance made it hard to pick out what she was saying, but it sounded like she was talking to someone about me. I trained my ears and heard the words 'Can't cope with him any more' and 'Do you know anyone who can take him?'

I waited until I could hear the conversation had come to an end.

'Who were you talking to?' I demanded.

No reply.

'Who were you talking to?' I shouted.

'What?'

An amazing attack of acute deafness.

'Who were you talking to?' I yelled.

'No one you know.'

That wasn't what I asked.

'You were talking about me, weren't you?'

'Yeah,' she grudgingly admitted.

'It was a hospice, wasn't it?' I pressed. 'You think I'm going to die. Well, I don't want to go to a hospice. I want to die here in bed.'

'Of course it wasn't a fucking hospice, you berk,' she snapped, 'because you're not dying. How many more times do I have to tell you that you don't have BSE? If you did I'd be sending you to the vet. No, it's your mind I'm worried about.'

'I'm worried about my mind, too. It's no fun going demented.'

'There's no "going" about it. Which is why I've managed to get hold of a decent psychiatrist for you. I was going to tell you when you were a little calmer and marginally less potty, but since you've forced the issue I'm telling you now. I've found you a shrink.'

Two days later I found myself pouring my heart out to Dr Macdonald. And what a relief it was. A whole hour to discuss my symptoms, with only the odd pointless interruption from the shrink to spoil my flow.

'You have classic symptoms,' he said at the end.

I knew I had all along.

'You're severely depressed,' he continued.

Fantastic. I could have told him that. In fact, I just had been.

'Of course I'm depressed. Anyone with BSE would be.'

'No. You're clinically severely depressed. Panic attacks, sleeplessness, depersonalization . . . you've got the lot.'

'Oh.'

'You need to be admitted to hospital. Do you have medical insurance?'

Do bears shit in the woods.

'Yuh.'

'Good. There will be a bed for you at the Lodge Hospital tomorrow.'

'You don't think there's a chance I'm depressed and I've got BSE?' I asked, on my way out.

'No,' he said firmly. 'But there'll be plenty of time to talk about all that in hospital.'

My wife didn't seem at all put out when I told her what was up. In fact, she looked positively delighted for someone who had been told that her husband was clinically depressed. 'At last we've got a proper diagnosis,' she said evenly, before rather spoiling the effect by rushing off to phone Debby – she thought I hadn't noticed – and whispering, 'Yeah, he's off to the nut-house. It'll be like having three weeks' holiday.' At least that's what I thought I heard, but maybe I just imagined it. In truth, I didn't much care. I was anxious about going to hospital, but I was certain it was where I wanted to be. I would be taken seriously by the shrinks and I would be under constant supervision. What more could a hypochondriac ask for?

The Lodge wasn't a lodge. Not what I call a lodge anyway. It was awesome. Its white façade was topped off with turrets and battlements and it sprawled lazily in its handsomely tailored grounds. A reassuring number of powerful L, M and N-reg cars nosed out of the parking bays. We weren't talking wards here; we were talking private rooms with TV and *en suite* bathroom. We were talking my kind of hospital.

The doorman – or was it the receptionist? – checked me in and a nurse escorted me up to my room. I looked out the window. Hmm. Bars. Not such a good sign. Before long Dr Macdonald turned up with a bunch of groupies and proceeded to talk them through my case.

'Right, John. I'm putting you on medication. I'm giving you Prozac for the depression. It takes about ten days to two weeks for the effects to show, so don't worry if you don't feel any different. I'm giving you Fluanxol for the anxiety and Meneril to help you sleep. Do you have any problems with this?'

Are you kidding? I've waited over a decade for this moment. A legitimate excuse to try out a few narcs stronger than a Nurofen.

'No, I'm sure that will be fine,' I said, with as little eagerness as I could manage.

After a few more routine questions – next of kin and so on – I was left on my own. Which was very depressing. All my cockiness deserted me. I slumped on my bed. No family, no friends, no job, no future. Just me and the TV. A knock on the door interrupted my vigil. Dinner. No plastic knives and forks. So I wasn't on suicide watch, then. Several hours passed. Another knock. Drug time. Goody-goody. I lay back on the bed watching the news and waiting for the sleepers to do their stuff.

The next thing I knew it was 3 a.m. The TV was still on and as per usual I was wide awake, rigid with fear. Great. I'd missed the fun bit of the drugs and now they had worn off. It was back to the nocturnal white-knuckle ride. And just as I was dozing off through sheer nervous exhaustion, the drugs trolley paid its 6.30 a.m. wake-up call. Welcome to hospital, John.

The nights maintained this dismally bleak pattern for the next two weeks. The days were another matter, however. On my second day I felt bold enough to poke my head beyond my door and to assimilate the rest of my surroundings. Initially this consisted of watching TV in the TV lounge rather than in my bedroom. But hey, it was a start. And slowly, slowly I got to know some of the other inmates. And by and large, a nicer group of nutters you couldn't hope to meet.

OK, some of the more severe schizophrenics were a little tricky to hold down a conversation with, and the depressives who turned their chairs to face the wall weren't great company either, but there were plenty of others to hang out with. The manic depressives were usually the most fun. They had invariably been dragged kicking and screaming into the hospital after a manic binge, during which they had generally spent thousands of pounds they didn't have, and would pace up and down the corridors talking to anyone prepared to listen.

My social life tended to centre on my own wing. There was Susannah, an attractive singer who was made to wear pyjamas because she was always trying to break out; Sarah, who used to moan about how one of the other patients kept trying to get off with her but compulsively flirted with him; Alan, a sleepwalking dentist; the immaculate Jane, who washed her hair five times a day to make herself look normal; Emily, who wanted to be transferred to the hell-hole of the Charing Cross NHS psych ward because she fancied the shrink there; Ed, who looked forward to each dose of ECT, electroconvulsive therapy; and me, with BSE. Dotty, every single one of us, but we didn't mind at all. We tolerated each other's idiocies when everyone else had given up on us. We were friends.

The days passed in a quasi-geriatric haze. Nothing was rushed, everything was ordered, little was expected –

you could give up on anything at any time; there was even room in the routine for an afternoon nap. And best of all, all the staff were so nice. No one raised their voice, and everyone was enthusiastic, congratulatory and kind. Completely outside the realms of my normal experience. Mental hospital is the closest I have ever got to civilization.

The mornings would kick off with a few group sessions labelled 'cognitive therapy' or 'coping with depression' or some such. Which were quite stressful really. At least for me. Because I had a slightly different agenda going. I had used my time in the hospital quite profitably by pumping other depressive patients for details of their symptoms and had been alarmed to discover that while panic attacks and sleeplessness were common currency, no one else had a clue what I was on about when I mentioned feeling permanently physically unbalanced. So BSE still couldn't be ruled out. But not for want of effort on my part, as I made a point of interrupting these sessions on every occasion that symptoms came up – which was frequently – to get mine officially accepted on the list that the therapist drew up on the blackboard. This was easier said than done; even when it was Dawn who was running the show.

I had never met anyone more eager to please than Dawn. She was almost stiflingly ingratiating. She was also a complete nervous wreck. She would flush with embarrassment the moment she opened her mouth and would talk in a breathy voice that sounded as if she was on the verge of hyperventilating. I dread to think what her underarms were like when the hour was up. None of which was guaranteed to inspire confidence in a rabble of anxiety-ridden, institutionalized patients. But never mind. Like all the staff, she was very, very nice, and niceness counts for a lot when you're banged up.

'Hello, everyone,' she would fluster. 'Let's start by going round the room and introducing ourselves and saying one thing that makes us anxious.'

Quite clearly, one thing that made Dawn anxious was nobody opening their mouths. So naturally everyone stayed mute – an act of sadism that might surprise some people, but whoever said that mental patients had to be kind?

The longer the silence, the pucer and more twittery Dawn became, until she couldn't resist breaking it herself.

'I'm Dawn and being late makes me very anxious,' she would open.

Since she was always a few minutes late for everything, this could have explained why she was always so anxious. But it did make me wonder. If she got in that much of a state over being a few minutes late, what on earth would happen to her if she encountered a real-life crisis? Like mislaying her car keys.

Given her delicate disposition, I'd imagined that Dawn would be a complete pushover when it came to getting my symptoms listed as those of depression. Not so, though the problem wasn't her obstinacy so much as her desire to get my symptoms to fit in with hers.

'Let's do a list of the physical symptoms of depression. Any suggestions?' she asked.

And we would then meander our way through all the usual suspects. Until. . .

'Feeling wobbly, as if I'm hallucinating the whole time,' I chipped in.

'Yes,' said Dawn encouragingly. 'Like you're hyperventilating.'

'No, not like I'm hyperventilating,' I replied firmly.

'Oh. You mean, like your heart is racing,' she tried again.

'No, not like my heart is racing.'

'Oh. You mean you feel a bit wobbly from time to time.'

'No. I mean I feel wobbly the whole time.'

'Oh. I see,' she said doubtfully.

Dawn was decent enough to leave it at that and to make sure my symptom went up on the blackboard, but she was evidently unconvinced. Which did nothing to help my BSE. After such an ordeal the only thing to do was to take a brisk walk to work off the excess adrenalin. So this precluded the so-called organized walk, which was in effect a snail's-pace plod around the grounds.

You wouldn't have thought it possible, but everything slowed down even more after lunch. Well, we had all had a gruelling morning, I suppose. You could snooze or talk – or both at the same time if you were Alan – and then around mid-afternoon each wing was gathered together to join in a communal activity organized by the nursing staff.

As an effort to socialize us in preparation for our parole dates, the group activities were a disaster. Various bods refused to turn up, others would wander off halfway through and a few would battle to switch on the TV. For my part, though, this was the highlight of the day, as most afternoons we would have a general knowledge quiz, which was irresistible to both my anorak and competitive streaks.

Being an anorak didn't really come into it, though, as the level of question wouldn't have tested the average ten-year-old.

'Your turn, Ian,' Siobhan, the nurse, said to some old boy who was looking out of the window. 'What's the capital of France?'

Ian neither acknowledged the question nor gave it a reply. There were a number of possible explanations for this. Ian was deaf. Ian didn't know. Ian was in a catatonic state. Ian didn't give a toss.

Which meant that it could be handed over.

'Does anyone else know the capital of France?' Siobhan asked.

'Paris,' I replied promptly.

'Oh, well done, John. Very well done indeed.'

This is the first and last time I've ever received plaudits for knowing that Paris was the capital of France.

'Your turn now, John,' Siobhan went on. 'Who is the President of the USA?'

I pretended to give this a little thought. No one likes a clever-clogs.

'Bill Clinton.'

'Excellent, John, excellent.'

No one bothered to keep the score, of course, as the name of the game was participation. But in case you were wondering, yours truly romped home as the runaway winner day after day. And if you think I grew tired of that, then you don't know me very well. Winning was only part of the fun, though. The quiz was also a great way of keeping tabs on my long-term memory, and thereby the progress of the BSE.

Two weeks in, everything changed. I woke up and I didn't have BSE any more. It took me a while to recognize it, mind. I'd got up, showered and was settling down to eat my breakfast, when I realized that I could look at my food without wondering whether I was hallucinating. It was most strange, and I decided to keep quiet about it. I didn't want to risk disclosure in case it was another of my mind's little pranks and in any case I didn't want to get sent home. I was blissfully happy in the nut-house. It was warm, it was cosy . . . it was like early retirement.

Dr Macdonald wasn't so easily fooled. I held him at bay for a couple of days by making myself scarce, but he eventually caught up with me and accosted me in the corridor.

'You're looking a great deal better,' he said, eyeballing me intently.

'Am I?'

'Yes.'

'Well, I suppose I am feeling better.'

'Good. And how are the BSE ruminations?'

He liked that pun.

'Now you mention it, my symptoms have disappeared.'

You can't lie to your shrink, can you?

'I told you they would when the Prozac started working,' he said. 'As the depression eases, the acute depersonalization lifts.'

'Perhaps Prozac cures both depression and BSE.'

'I don't think so,' he replied, a tad acidly. 'We'd better think of getting you home soon. Let's aim for the end of the week.'

'I'm not sure I'll be re. . .'

'You'll be fine,' he replied. 'And it's time you came off your night-time medication.'

Shit, shit, shit, shit, shit, shit.

'I think you're right,' I lied. Sometimes all of us have to bow to the inevitable and accept that all good things must come to an end. Sooner rather than later.

Three weeks to the day since she had dropped me off, my wife motored up to the Lodge to collect me and cart me off home. But not before we'd had one final meeting with Dr Macdonald.

'Are you really sure he's ready to come home?' asked my wife, looking totally relaxed with a most unseasonal suntan.

'Yes,' said Dr Macdonald.

'Really sure?' she repeated, begging him to say no.

'I hear that Morocco is lovely at this time of year,' I interrupted, apropos of not much at all.

'Right then,' my wife said hurriedly. 'I suppose we'd better be off. Have you got everything, John?'

'Yeah,' I replied, before turning to Dr Macdonald. 'And thank you for everything.'

'It's been a pleasure,' he said, the consummate professional – and liar – to the end.

I picked up my bags, chucked them into the boot of the car and resumed my rightful place behind the steering wheel. This isn't just chauvinism, it's an important safety precaution. Ask the kids.

'Are you OK?' my wife said considerately, as we ground to a halt in a traffic jam.

'Er. Sort of,' I said uncertainly. I'd forgotten how large and scary the world was outside the confines of the Lodge.

'So what do you think you've learnt while you were in the hospital?'

My wife's keen on learning. To make up for her inadequate education, I suppose.

'Not sure really.'

I could have said, 'I'm a walking disaster area.' Or 'I didn't have BSE after all.' Or 'Paris is the capital of France.' But I got the feeling that she was expecting a more profound résumé of my experience than any of those.

'Oh, come on. You must have got something out of your three weeks inside.'

I thought hard.

'Well, I am going to finish with Mary.'

'Are you sure that's a good idea?'

Absolutely fucking certain.

'Well, I have talked it over with Dr Macdonald and various other counsellors at the Lodge, and they all seem to recommend it.'

'Hmm,' she grunted, consoled. And then she brightened considerably. 'This means that you'll be able to pay our mortgage rather than Mary's then.'

Mary was rather less pleased about this new arrangement. I couldn't handle breaking the news to her face to face – in case I chickened out. So I wrote her a letter explaining my intentions and requesting three or four final sessions to draw together the threads of the therapy and to say goodbye. Mucho grown-up, I thought. Two days later I got a phone call from her granting me an audience.

'Hello, John,' she said, as I walked in.

'Hello, Mary.'

'So.'

'So.'

I was getting the hang of this.

'So you want to leave me?'

'Yes.'

'You've made your mind up?'

'Yes.'

'Then there's nothing to discuss, is there?'

Er?

'Well, there's what went wrong between us, what went right between us and where we go from here.'

'But we're not going anywhere,' she said stiffly. 'You've made that perfectly clear.'

'I meant more along the lines of parting on good terms. That's why I asked for a number of winding-up sessions.'

'Well, I'm not prepared to give you them. You either carry on in therapy with me and we sort things out there, or we finish now.'

'I guess we finish now, then,' I said, somewhat rattled by her aggression.

'I should warn you that I think you're making a very big mistake that could prove extremely costly.'

'We'll see, I suppose,' I muttered, more calmly than I felt.

'We will.'

'So that's it.'

'Not quite,' she replied. 'I've got this for you.'

'What is it?' ·

'Your bill.'

'What for?'

'The sessions you missed while you were in hospital.'

'You're fucking kidding.'

'Do I sound like I'm kidding?'

Silly question. Mary never sounded like she was kidding.

'But how could I come when I was in hospital? I didn't decide to go bonkers.'

On reflection this might have been a lie. Going bonkers might have been the only way I could escape Mary's clutches.

'You know the rules. You have to pay for all missed sessions.'

'But it was partly down to you that I was in the asylum anyway.'

'Oh. So it was my fault, was it? Look, nobody ever said therapy was an easy journey. Sometimes it can take you to some nasty places. Sometimes you might need to be hospitalized. It's all part of the process.'

'It's not how I see the process.'

'I understand that. But I shall still expect you to pay your final bill.'

'Well, I'm not going to.'

And I haven't. And if you want to sue me, Mary, that's fine by me. My address is. . . Ah, fuck it, you can look it up yourself. I haven't moved.

Years and years of therapy. And I'm still no better at endings.

TWELVE

'You'll have to start challenging some of your negative assumptions,' said Clare, my cognitive therapist at the Lodge, whom I visited once a week as an out-patient.

We were on my third session. Each time she had made me fill in a multiple-choice questionnaire on my depression, and each time my score had shown no sign of reducing from dangerously psychotic levels.

'I'm sure you're right,' I replied, 'but I'm buggered if I know how.'

It was all terribly confusing. I wasn't having any of the symptoms I associated with depression – panic attacks, sleeplessness, BSE; in fact, I was feeling pretty normal. Well, normal for me. And yet I was being presented with my own handwritten evidence that I was still a mess.

And I couldn't see any way out. Without lying. Because it was impossible to answer any of the questions truthfully without sounding depressed or completely unhinged. For instance, one of the questions was 'How often do you think about dying? 1. Almost never. 2. Occasionally. 3. Often. 4. Every day.' Now, it was obvious that you were meant to tick 'Almost never' and get an enormous round of applause and a clean bill of health. And it was quite tempting, too. But I didn't see how anyone could honestly tick anything but 'Every day'. You only have to read the newspapers, watch the news, hire a video – anything really – and you're going to be confronted by death on a daily basis. Maybe not yours, but someone else's, and if you can't make an emotional link between someone else's demise and your own, then you must be some kind of psychopath. Also, if you really weren't thinking about your own death each day, then you probably would die, mown down by traffic while crossing the road without looking.

Maybe what most people labelled clinical depression was nothing more than brutal realism. Which would make a certain kind of sense, as it would be hard not to be depressed when you see things as they really are. This wasn't Clare's assessment of the situation, though.

'You must try to be a little gentler on yourself,' she said soothingly, adopting a slightly different tack. 'Try telling yourself you're a worthwhile person, focusing on your good points.'

Talk about asking the impossible. I was up against the same brick wall of honesty. I didn't think I was an exceptionally unworthwhile person, but then again I wasn't particularly worthwhile either. Besides, what kind of moron – other than a desperate loser – rushes round the place shouting, 'I'm worthwhile, I'm really fucking worthwhile.'

I'm OK. Ish. That's all. By and large, I muddle through. Some things I don't do too badly, but in most areas there is vast room for improvement. I'm ashamed of myself a lot of the time, I'm deeply envious of other people and I could be a lot nicer than I am. All in all, I'm a bit of a disappointment to myself; I'm not the bloke I imagined I would be when I was younger.

'Er . . . I'm not sure I can do that,' I said at last.

'Come on, try,' Clare cajoled. 'Just one good thing.'

'Well, I haven't murdered anyone, I suppose.'

'Be serious,' she snapped.

I am being serious. I haven't murdered anyone. Or maybe she thinks killing people is good. In which case, no wonder I'm depressed.

'OK then,' I said, suddenly inspired. 'Since I've been let out of the Lodge, then it must mean someone thinks I'm sane.'

'I wouldn't count on it.'

I ignored this snide little aside; Clare was just very jealous that no one had ever given her a certificate of sanity. Nonetheless, I was struggling badly in my search to find good things to say about myself.

So why not get someone else to say them instead? This was a brilliant idea, even if I say so myself. Devastatingly simple and devastatingly effective. Surround myself with a whole load of toadying flunkeys telling me how wonderful I am. That's what the Royal Family, politicians, movie stars and other megalomaniacs do. Which is why they're always looking so confident and pleased with themselves.

I couldn't rely on my family or friends for this special kind of treatment, though. None of them had shown any inclination to make such rash judgements in the past and I couldn't see them starting now. Even if I asked them. Which I couldn't, because it would be far too demeaning. 'Please, please, be my friend and say something nice about me.' Yuk. In any case, what could they say? 'You're a good husband/dad/son/brother/friend.' Hardly. There was far too much history to believe any of that.

But I could start again. I could make myself be nice. I could befriend various lonely people in the pub and listen to their long and dreary life stories without yawning. I could do some worthy charity work – provided the expenses were good. I could become a local councillor and campaign tirelessly to have our road pedestrianized. I could become an exhibit in the Millennium Dome. The shining embodiment of Tony's vision for a new, cool Britain. And all for no reward other than to hear the nation chorus, 'That John Crace, he's one helluva good bloke.'

All this needed careful planning. When you're going grey, your hair's falling out, your gut's bulging, you're the wrong side of forty and you're utterly unremarkable, it's hard work marketing yourself as a happening person. So I set up a number of working parties to investigate my best options, then sat back and waited for them to report.

Sometimes things fall into your lap. Because while the committees were off doing whatever committees do, I became a star overnight. Hard to credit, I know, but there you are. One day I was a complete nobody and the next day I was a celebrity. Not a very big celebrity – a D-list type like Tania Bryer, Danni Minogue and Jason Donovan. But, hey, don't knock it. I mean, who the fuck are you, anyway?

The reason for my instant fame was a book I had written about being a dad. No one had ever read a single one of my previous books and I had no reason to expect this one to be any different. But I got home from work one day to find six messages on the answer-machine from local radio stations, asking – no begging – no gagging – for me to be interviewed by them. I had hit the big time. Pay dirt.

I phoned them back the next day.

'Hi. It's John Crace. You called me yesterday.'

'Who?'

'John Crace.'

'Oh, John Crace,' the voice said doubtfully. 'Ah yes, John. Can you appear on our morning show tomorrow? You'll need to go into our London studio, and our presenter will talk to you down the line.'

'Um, let me check,' I said, shuffling a few blank pieces of paper. 'Yes, that should be fine.'

'Great, John. Will 10.30 be OK?'

'Yuh, fine. Er. . . Could you organize a cab to pick me up?' I added grandiosely.

'Our budget doesn't run to that,' the voice retorted.

'Oh, never mind,' I said quickly, before I was chucked off the line-up.

'Super. Oh, by the way, I L-U-R-V-E your book.'

'Can you say that last bit again?'

'Sorry?'

'Oh, nothing. Just thinking out loud.'

'OK. Speak to you tomorrow then.'

My media career was about to begin.

The next day I trotted off to Bush House, where I was processed at reception, shunted off to the back of the building and squeezed into a tiny, airless, windowless booth with nothing in it except a chair, a few dials and a set of headphones.

'Put on the headphones and wait for the station to get in contact with you,' Big Brother croaked over the tannoy.

I did as I was told and sweated for five minutes.

'Hi, are you there, John?' my headphones rattled.

'Yes.'

'Good. I'll be coming to you in about a couple of minutes when this record's finished. OK?'

No. I was hoping for a bit more notice and a bit more build-up. I want glitz and razzmatazz.

'Yeah, that's fine.'

'Great. Speak to you in a minute. Just relax and try to

imagine we're having a conversation in your living-room.'

'What? You're going to have the telly on as well?'

'What did you say?'

'Sorry. Only joking.'

'Sure.'

I heard the record end and the presenter start her intro. 'I have with me in our London studio. . .' She rabbited on for a bit about the book and then asked me a question. And I had no idea of the answer. I was dimly aware that she had alluded to some part of the book, but I had no idea precisely which, as it was so long since I had written it.

I dredged my memory for something vaguely funny and relevant. It wasn't what was expected, though, as the presenter was openly surprised by my reply, but it was good enough for the purposes of living-room conversation. I didn't want to get caught out again, though, so I tried to steer the interview round to the later sections of the book, as they were much fresher in my mind. Whereupon I was quickly manoeuvred back to the beginning again. At this point it clicked that the presenter had read only the first five chapters, and she was going to fix it so that if anyone looked foolish it was going to be me.

Somehow I made it through without disgracing myself, but we were both relieved when my ten minutes were up.

'Thanks ever so much, John,' the presenter said graciously as we went off air. 'That was smashing.'

'No probs,' I replied, in what I hoped was my best old-radio-hack voice.

I worked hard after that near disaster. I reread the book – especially the opening chapters – and I became so proficient that I could quote huge chunks verbatim. Not that I did. I learnt that presenters liked a few juicy soundbites, so that's what I gave them. I rapidly became a bit of a pro, but I soon found that radio was not quite my *métier*. It was intimate, it was cosy, but – to be frank – it was just too small for me. A man of my talents deserved a far bigger stage, a bigger audience. My public needed to see me. I needed to be on telly.

So that's where I was going. You know how some people effortlessly gravitate to the top? How they go from being a complete nobody to a small-screen ever-present? People like Anthea Turner. Well, I was joining them. But in my case there was no Svengali manipulating my air-time; there was just a buzz about me. Radio and TV producers would natter to each other about me over lunch at the Ivy. At least I assume that's what was going on. Because I was definitely hot.

And the calls started coming in. Well, a call came in. From a cable-TV station. To do a talk show. But that was all right. I was happy to start there. I wasn't too proud to pay my dues. A legacy of Mary, I suppose. So off I went to make my televisual début.

It was everything I had dreamed of. TV companies don't have receptionists, they have concierges, and Jules, or whatever his name was, led me off to my dressing-room. Think about it. I had my own dressing-room. I was being loved to death. What more could anyone else want? Their own make-up artist? Well, I had that, too. She was brilliant. Within ten minutes I was looking fifteen years younger – passably attractive even. If I'd seen my reflection in a shop window I might have fancied myself. I was then whizzed off to the green room where I dissolved into a giant armchair. A few minutes later the presenter swished in and swooned, 'Oh, John. Your book is so-o-o-o funny. I'm so-o-o-o looking forward to talking to you.'

Oh, kissy, kissy, kissy, kissy. I'd just had everything I'd come for then, darlings.

Unfortunately, there was still the interview to go. So a mike was shoved down my front, I was led out on to the set, cooked under the lights and asked a few gentle questions. Which I handled pretty well, I thought. I was witty and charming – by my standards – and I didn't dry up. The presenter seemed to think so too. 'That was ma-a-a-arvellous, John. Thank you so-o-o-o much for coming,' she said, before giving me a regal wave of dismissal.

'How did it go?' my wife asked me on my return.

That she even remembered what I had been doing suggested that she was secretly impressed. She's never been on TV. Nor is she likely to be.

'Yup, it went well.'

'Oh,' she said, failing to conceal her disappointment. 'That's nice.'

We don't have cable TV *chez* Crace – an ongoing battle over Sky Sports that I am losing dismally – but a few days later I was sent a video of my award-winning performance.

'Let's watch it now,' I said, ripping open the package.

'Do we have to?' moaned my wife.

'Yes.'

'But I'll be late for work.'

'I'm only on for twelve minutes, thirty-one seconds.'

'Precisely?'

'Precisely.'

'OK then.'

So I bunged it in and settled back to watch my wife go green.

'Look,' she shrieked.

'What?'

'Your head.'

'What about it?'

'It's wobbling about all over the place.'

She was right. It was wobbling. I'd been concentrating so hard on saying the right things that I'd forgotten about my physical presentation. I looked like I was in end-stage Parkinson's.

'It's not as bad as all that,' I said.

'Oh, yes it is,' she replied gleefully. 'You were absolutely crap. Still, as no one was watching the programme anyway, it doesn't really matter.'

For once my wife was right. It didn't matter. Because when you're on a roll people will forgive you anything. It was only a matter of weeks before the phone rang again.

'Hi. It's Sandy from *Kilroy*. I've read your book. I think it's great.'

I was getting used to this sort of flattery. But not tired of it.

'Thanks.'

'Yeah, and we'd love you to come on the show to talk about fatherhood.'

'And what do you want me to talk about exactly?'

'Oh, nothing too specific. Just the problems of being a dad.'

'You do realize that the book's meant as a bit of a laugh?'

'Sure. But it raises some serious issues.'

Fuck. She really had read it. What a wonderfully sensitive woman. I could fall in love with her over the phone.

'Yeah. Well, as long as you know I'm no childcare expert.'

'That's great then,' she said. 'We'll send a car for you at eleven on Friday. The programme will be filmed at one, and you'll be taken back to the paper straight after.'

A limo. A sodding limo.

After a morning's preening, rummaging through my extensive M&S wardrobe, I settled on the casual, bohemian look of jeans and a sweater. What I wear everyday, in fact. Though I made one concession. The sweater was a polo-neck – to hide the neck brace. I wasn't going to take any chances with wobbly-head syndrome this time.

At eleven on the dot a large black Merc pulled up outside the house. Decision time. Front seat or back? Back seat might have impressed the neighbours more, but I'm a democrat at heart, so I hopped in the front, and spent the next hour listening to the driver rattle off a long list of TV stars he had taken to the Teddington studios.

And that was that as far as celebdom was concerned. Or being treated like a human being, for that matter.

'You here for *Kilroy*? What's your name? Yes. You're on the list. Take a seat in the waiting-room. Someone will see you presently.'

Waiting-room? Holding area more like it, for the room resembled an airport departure lounge. There were a fair number of identical pieces of office furniture dotted around, but not enough to accommodate the teeming masses. Abandoned mothers, angry fathers and a few old dears rounded up from God knows where to make up the numbers – all human life was there. And in pride of place, perched high on the middle of one wall, was a giant TV screen, showing – you've guessed it – *Kilroy*.

Which reminded me. Where was Kilroy? I wasn't supposed to be one of the audience riff-raff: I was a personality, a specially invited guest. One of the people who has a little blue caption under their name. At least that's what I had been told. I should have been off somewhere quiet with Killy-Willy, having a cosy chat about the pressures of being in the public eye.

It turned out that Kilroy was delayed filming another show. But even if he hadn't been he wouldn't have showed up, because our Bob doesn't demean himself by actually meeting the punters until the show is to begin. I mean, why should he, when he's got all those researchers to do all the work?

Shortly after one, I started to get anxious, as I had to get away on time. Us VIPs have very hectic diaries. Sorry, Filofaxes. I voiced my concerns to one of the women with a clipboard patrolling the lounge.

'Don't worry,' she said. 'We'll make sure you get the first car after the show. By the way, we're really looking forward to what you've got to say.'

By now, I wasn't sure whether I wanted to say anything at all; I was beginning to feel like a prisoner in Stalag Kilroy, and all I could think about was whether I would ever get out.

At last we were all coralled and led down to the studio in single file. Once we were all in our allotted places, the man himself appeared. Armani-suited, covered in slap and perfectly coiffed, Kilroy was a vision of slickness. He slid effortlessly into a well-rehearsed patter.

'Now, I want you all to relax,' he oozed. 'If you want to speak, wave to get my attention and I'll come over. We want to make it look as if we're having a friendly discussion.'

Which was the last anyone heard of friendly discussion. From the word go, it was like a dogfight. The researchers had done their homework: various women had a go at men about this and that, men attacked women over access and everyone put the boot into the token lawyer. Throughout all this, Kilroy tried to maintain an air of rational detachment, while doing everything he could to stir.

I finally decided it was time to get my money's worth.

'It's too simplistic to say that men should do this and women should do that. Roles are much more ambiguous these days,' I said.

Kilroy gave me a Darth Vader stare.

'So. You're saying that you don't know what a father does?' he snapped.

'Well. . .'

'Do you know what a mother does then?'

'Not exactly.'

'You don't know much then. You're just confused.'

And with that he waltzed off to someone else before I had a chance to reply. I had broken the unwritten law of the programme. Sensible debate makes crap TV.

I tried to get back in at various points during the remainder of the programme, but Kilroy carefully ignored me. It was his show and no one was going to upstage him.

I registered my disaffection by being the only member of the studio audience not to clap at the end of the show, but I dare say this little moment of anarchy was edited out.

'Thanks very much, everyone. Great show. It'll be broadcast next Wednesday, so make sure you watch it,' said Kilroy, before skipping off.

'How was it? When will it be shown?' I was asked on my return to work.

'Lousy. I got trashed. It's on next Thursday, but I wouldn't bother to watch.'

And that was pretty much that as far as my time in the limelight went. I wouldn't have minded a bit longer, a few more prestigious gigs, being hounded by the paparazzi, but somehow being love-bombed by strangers was even more mentally debilitating than being disliked and disregarded by family, friends and myself. At least that was genuine.

Still, sometimes life does give you a second chance. About six months later I got another call.

'Hi. It's Katy from *Kilroy*. I wa. . .'

Click. Don't call me, Kilroy. I'll call you.

THIRTEEN

'I reckon I'm a bit of a good-time girl, you know,' said my wife, as she slurped her tea in her shapeless towelling dressing-gown.

Like most of her breakfast-time stream of consciousness, I didn't think this worthy of a reply, so I carried on reading the paper.

'I said, I reckon I'm a bit of a good-time girl,' she repeated forcefully.

'I heard you the first time.'

'Well?'

'Well what?'

'Well, what do you think?'

'I think you're mad.'

'Why?' she said, hurt.

'Because no one could be less of a good-time girl.'

'Other people say I am.'

'Who?'

'Debby and Elena.'

Spare me.

'I thought they were supposed to be your friends.'

'They are.'

'Well, either they're taking loyalty too far or else they don't know you very well.'

'Perhaps it's you who doesn't know me very well.'

Cutting.

'Look. You get panicky if you're in bed after 10.30, you can't sleep without earplugs, you're an associate member of the Ramblers Association and you're desolate if you miss the *Archers* omnibus. That is not being a good-time girl.'

'But I've got good-time attitudes. Existentially speaking, I'm an out-and-out hedonist.'

What the fuck is that supposed to mean?

'You're not. You're gloomy, angry and difficult. That's why I like you.'

'Bollocks,' she hissed. 'I'm fun-loving.'

'How come if you're so fun-loving you ended up marrying someone like me then?'

Yeah. Argue your way out of that one.

'I was younger. I didn't know any better.'

Younger. This was the ongoing problem. You'd have thought there was only room in the house for one mid-life crisis. Mine. But, oh no, my wife had to muscle in on my turf and have one of her own. Only hers manifested itself in an increasingly desperate desire not just to halt the ageing process, but to reverse it. She appeared to believe she could get younger and younger.

I've told you about her taste in music. Well, that was only the tip of the iceberg. The bathroom was clogged with skin-care products, you couldn't open the fridge for all the latest nutritional health fads and the bedroom was littered with Miss Selfridge catalogues. Everything was a testament to youth. You could tell her that she was intelligent or good-looking and she wouldn't bat an eyelid. But tell her that she looked like she was in her early thirties and she would go all gooey. She might even sleep with you. Who knows? It worked for me. Sometimes.

There was nothing intrinsically wrong with my wife having a mid-life crisis. Even I'm not enough of a hypocrite to deny her the pleasure. I felt a bit put out that she couldn't have been a bit more original – imagine how annoyed serial killers must get with copycats – but my main objection was that our mid-life crises were just incompatible. Because the younger she tried to make herself, the older I felt.

But being a modern, nineties kind of guy, I did my best to accommodate my wife's delusions. No let's not be modest. I indulged them. I became the Cilla Black of our relationship. So when she said that she felt like doing something really young and spontaneous, I went along with it.

'What do you want to do?'

'Something wild,' she replied. 'Like going to Paris for two nights without the kids.'

'Fine, let's do it.'

'I don't think we can.'

'Why not?'

'I don't think I can leave the kids for that long.'

'They might be pleased for the break.'

'You just don't understand, do you?' she said.

'Understand what?'

'That it's different for a mum to leave her kids.'

'Oh. So you think you love them more than me, do you?'

'Don't start this one again. It's different, that's all.'

Meaning, yes, I do love them more than you.

'It's only for two nights, for fuck's sake,' I said in a spirit of compromise. 'We're not putting them in care.'

'I'm still not sure.'

'Make your mind up. It was your idea in the first place.'

'OK then.'

'Fine. When shall we go?'

'A couple of months' time.'

'Yeah. That would be pretty spontaneous.'

So I booked two Apex Eurostar tickets – approximately £240 – persuaded the nanny to work twenty-four hours a day for two days – £150 – reserved a room in a small but chic hotel off the Boulevard St Germain – approximately £250, and we just hopped on the tube to Waterloo and bunked off to Paris on the spur of the moment. God, we were so young.

And what did we do in Paris, the city of romance and fatal car crashes? We slept. That's what. From the moment we arrived at our hotel we barely stretched a leg outside. It was payback time for the years of child-induced fatigue. No quarrelling, no bickering – except between ourselves – and no interruptions. It was also the most expensive snooze I'd ever had.

I'm sure it wasn't exactly the fun-loving, club-hopping, E-dropping time my wife had had in mind, but she's a good spin doctor.

'Did you have a nice time?' said Ruth on our return.

'Wonderful,' said my wife.

'What did you do?'

'Oh, nothing much. We stayed in bed most of the time.'

'How horny.'

'Mmmm,' my wife creamed, dreamily.

But if being thought by others to be young was good enough for my wife, it wasn't for me. I wanted to feel young. And I thought I knew how to do this. The answer wasn't to hang around with young people and hope to absorb their vitality through osmosis, but to hang around with old people. How could anyone of forty not feel young and athletic compared with a bunch of bald, arthritic octogenarians? This was cognitive therapy in action.

There were certain hurdles to be overcome, though. You know how your grandparents are meant to be sweet, unthreatening old dears – the sort of people who ply you with sweets and let you get away with murder? Well, mine weren't quite like that. I don't think they much liked me – they were always much fonder of my sisters – and I didn't much like them. To be honest, they scared me. It wasn't that they were particularly authoritarian – certainly not for their generation – it was just that they were old. I could tell that their bodies weren't as they were supposed to be. They sagged in the wrong places, they stooped and shuffled, they couldn't see or hear properly and they shouted. They weren't altogether human, somehow.

Or perhaps it was that they were all too human. On some level I may have recognized that they were dying in front of my eyes. Because there are many ways of dying. Of course, it's the heart attacks and the cancers which actually kill you. But the dying is a much slower process. It's about your body grinding to a halt and mutating into a corpse while you're still alive. Which is why many old people tend to smell a bit odd. It's not the leaking colostomy bags, though they don't help – it's the smell of decomposing flesh.

So there was a certain element of acclimatization required, which of necessity was done with a certain amount of secrecy. Because old people are not cool. Not nowadays. Apprentice criminals are taught to use them for mugging practice, and old lags just out of borstal or prison use them to get their confidence back, before graduating back to the proper targets. Young people. Because it's actually not worth mugging old people – they don't have any money. Robert Maxwell and successive governments have made sure of that by rendering any pension valueless. Does anyone complain? Not really. Well, old people do, but nobody listens, and everyone else – my wife included – thinks they're going to stay young for ever. And as old people don't have any money, nobody gives a toss about them. TV, newspapers and other forms of popular culture concentrate on attracting that elusive, hip yoof market – cash with dash, and the old can go fuck themselves, apart from once a year on Remembrance Day, when a grateful nation congratulates them for still breathing.

Which is obviously very bad news for the aged. But what a wonderful opportunity for someone like me. I didn't have mega-dosh, but compared with old people I was fantastically wealthy. So I could impress the hell out of them. Most wouldn't have ever seen a £20 note, let alone a £50 note, so I could wander into a sheltered housing scheme and cause a hell of a stir. The mere fact that I could wander in – and out – would take some beating on its own, but throw in the dosh and I'd be home and dry. They would love me for ever. I could take them down the pub – saloon bar, please – buy them a port and lemon or a milk stout, and tell them all about how I once saw the Rolling

Stones at Earls Court and how I once smoked a joint with Peter Sarstedt. They would have to rate me. Sod it. They could even overrate me. I wouldn't mind.

I wouldn't want you to think I was planning to patronize old people. That wouldn't have been very nice at all. And I'm sure old people can spot that kind of approach a mile off, as they have to put up with it every day. No. I'm not claiming altruism, just a straight swap. A quid pro quo. I would donate my time, money and hands-on knowledge of a 'Where It's At Lifestyle' – or perhaps a 'Where It Was Ten Years Ago Lifestyle', but they should be too gaga to know the difference – and in return they would give me respect, vigour and hope.

How do you make yourself a friend to the old when you don't even know any old people? You can't exactly go canvassing, and you can't meet old people naturally because they don't inhabit the same world as you and I. They only come out after the rest of us have gone to work, because they're banned from using public transport before 9.30 in the morning. The only ones you're likely to bump into are those few stragglers who are late home for their tea, when you're lucky enough to knock off on time.

Here's where networking helped. My parents knew lots of old people. Luckily, I've always been terribly considerate, tolerant and loving towards my parents, so I didn't think they would mind if I exploited them shamelessly for their contacts. Better still, I didn't think they would mind – or notice – if I exploited them shamelessly for being them. They could be my guinea-pigs as I learnt the ins and outs of hanging out with geriatrics.

'Er, Mum.'

'Yes, darling.'

She still calls me darling. Sometimes. I can't be all bad.

'How would you feel about me coming on holiday with you and Dad?'

'Are you broke at the moment?' she enquired accusingly.

'No.'

'Then why do you want to come on holiday with us?'

'To spend some time with you both. To bond.'

She couldn't refuse me now.

'Oh,' she said, nonplussed. 'That would be lovely.'

'Great. Where shall we go?'

My mother whipped out her diary.

'We're very booked up, you know,' she peered officiously. 'We're going to Nice to stay with Elizabeth for ten days later this month, so you can't come then. We're going to Stratford for the weekend when we get back, and two weeks later we're going to the Channel Islands for part of the week. So that's out, too. We might be able to squeeze you on to our Black Sea cruise in June, but perhaps it might be better if you joined us on our opera break in Verona in August.'

Christ. They were on a European permatour and I could hardly remember the last time I'd poked my nose outside the M25.

'You're very busy.'

'Of course we are,' she replied. 'We're retired.'

'I see,' I said, doing anything but.

'We don't sit in all day watching Richard and Judy,' she explained.

Then who does?

'We've got a fair bit saved up,' she continued, ' so we might as well spend it. You don't think that we're going to live like paupers and leave it all to you, do you? Ha, ha.'

Ha, ha, indeed.

'Ha, ha,' I laughed nervously. 'Of course not.'

'We just like to enjoy ourselves.'

This was too much. How could old people even think about enjoying themselves?

Our trip to Verona wasn't a great success. It wasn't the opera or the accommodation or the food that was bad; it was the pace. It was relentlessly exhausting. My parents would bounce down to breakfast at 7.30, guidebooks in hand, and eagerly plan the route march for the day. We would then be off, having first persuaded any strangers who seemed amusing to join us, and we wouldn't sit down again till lunch-time. During which they all talked to each other about various sites of interest that I didn't even know we'd visited. The afternoon was a repeat of the morning. I'd get forty-five minutes' break before an early dinner and then off we went to the opera.

Home had seldom seemed so attractive. And that's saying something, as one of my favourite bits of any holiday is to get back safely. To know that I haven't caught any filthy diseases, that the plane hasn't crashed, that the house hasn't been burgled, that the water pipes haven't burst and that I haven't been fired.

My mum was fairly gracious about the whole experience, but she made it clear that she didn't think we should go for a repeat performance. Nor was she at all keen to introduce me to any of her friends.

'I don't think they're quite your type,' she said.

Meaning, you're much too dull and boring for them.

For a few days I was abjectly morose about the failure of Operation Geriatric, but then out of the blue I got a phone call from my dad.

'Oi,' he said conspiratorially. 'We need to talk. But don't mention a word to your mother; she'd be furious if she knew what I was up to.'

Mystified, I met my dad in the Happy Eater just outside Guildford – his favourite restaurant – the next day.

'The holiday we've just been on,' he said, stuffing a few chips in his mouth. 'You only wanted to come along because you thought it would make you feel better about yourself, didn't you?'

I grunted noncommittally.

'I thought so,' he continued. 'I tried it with my parents when I was your age. It didn't work, though. I just felt worse.'

'Mmm.'

'Now, I love you a great deal and I can't bear to see

189

you go through the same torment as I did,' he said. 'So I'm going to break the old people's code and tell you our secret. We aren't like you think we are.'

'How do you mean?' I asked, becoming interested.

'I mean we're not all doddery and falling apart.'

'But what about those old codgers I see out and about?'

'They're decoys,' he replied. 'We all have to be one for a year. It's my turn soon. So expect to find me getting lost in familiar places and being photographed with politicians and royals. It's very *infra dig*, but absolutely necessary. It perpetuates all the right myths about being old, guarantees us free transport and discounts to cinemas and theatres, and distracts attention from the rest of us old people who want to be left alone to get on with enjoying ourselves.'

Enjoying. It was that word again.

'But how can you enjoy yourself, when you're so near to dying,' I asked bluntly. 'Aren't you afraid?'

'Of course we're afraid,' my dad said intently. 'Everyone's afraid of dying. But when you get to our age you know you're not going to die young. You can't be robbed any more. In fact, most of us are into bonus time and so we tend to just go for it. Pack as much in as we can. Including sex. You probably think that old people stop around fifty, don't you?'

I didn't really want to think about it at all.

'Something like that,' I said.

'Well, we don't. Our performance may not be what it

once was, but it's not bad. And when you're our age anything goes. Not for me and your mother, mind. We've always been faithful to one another. But you should see some of the people we know – orgies, wife-swapping, the lot. You see, old people don't give a toss about Aids because the time-scale makes it irrelevant. It's the same with smoking and drinking. We all do it – not around younger people like yourself – that would be irresponsible – but lung cancer, cirrhosis, who cares? You've got to die of something, so it might as well be of something enjoyable.'

'I never realized,' I muttered.

'Of course you didn't,' he said nicely. 'No one ever does. Take drugs, for instance. I do.'

'What?' I said, aghast.

'Yeah, what's the problem? Your generation doesn't have exclusive rights on them, you know. When you get to my age doctors will prescribe you almost anything. My heart. You probably thought that was old age or a congenital condition.'

'Yeah.'

'Amphetamine abuse. Or speed, I think you call it. I overdid it five years ago on a tour of America.'

'What?'

'All of us in Verona were at it. You don't think we could keep up that kind of schedule without it, do you?'

'I suppose not,' I said, secretly relieved.

'I'm telling you all this because I want to give you something to look forward to. Everyone knows that being forty is the worst time of your life. You're too old to be irresponsible, you've got to make a career and you've got kids. They're a nightmare. You certainly were.'

'Thanks.'

'I just want you to know the truth. The point is that it's not going to get better for a while, either. So you've just got to put up with it. But come sixty-five it'll be downhill all the way. Just hang on to that.'

So that just left the small matter of the next twenty-five years to deal with.

FOURTEEN

'So what is it that makes you stressed?' said Clare.

How long have you got? Living, thinking, walking, talking, working, not working, dying.

'Just about everything,' I replied.

'I don't mean generally speaking. I want you to come up with specific events, so that we can focus on ways of coping with them to make them less stressful.'

'I see. Well, I suppose it's the repetition that gets me. I'm sick to death of having the same arguments with my wife over and over again. I'm fed up with having the same delays on public transport on the way into work. I hate the way the same bills keep coming in month after month. And that's just for starters.'

'That's good. Now, how do you think you could

change your attitudes and behaviour to make these less stressful.'

'I've no idea,' I said.

But I did. Only I wasn't telling her.

As soon as I got home, I dashed to the telephone.

'Hello,' I enquired. 'Is that the Roslin Institute?'

'Yes,' replied a broad Scots voice.

'Can I speak to the person who cloned Dolly the sheep?'

'Speaking.'

'Great. This may seem an odd request, but I was so impressed by the job you did on Dolly that I was wondering if you could do the same for me.'

'How do you mean?' he asked cautiously.

'I mean I want you to clone me. I don't want some younger version of me. I want someone who's going to look exactly the same as I do now.'

'Hmm. Funny you should mention this. We've just been given a Government grant to conduct just such an experiment. There's only one drawback.'

'What's that?'

'You and your clone would have to appear as exhibits in the Millennium Dome.'

'Shouldn't be a problem.'

'Fine. Just send us up a sample, then, and your clone will be with you within a week.'

So I chopped off the end of one finger, plopped it into a sample container filled with saline solution and sent it off to Edinburgh. Five days later there was a knock on the door.

'Hi, I'm John,' said my clone.

'So am I,' I said.

'You look great.'

'You too.'

It was narcissism at first sight. I could tell right away that we were going to get on just fine.

We sat down to establish some ground rules. He was quite happy to be called John Two, but he was bitterly disappointed that he wasn't going to be allowed either to sleep with my wife or smoke, drink or take drugs. I had to draw the line somewhere. The main thing we had to hammer out was continuity. We couldn't have me disappearing into the living-room only to magically reappear from the bedroom moments later. So I bought him a microscopic earpiece through which I could keep him up to date with what I was doing and let him know when he was going to be required to work.

And it went like clockwork. John Two would go to work on my behalf, but I would get all the credit. And while he was off slaving, I would be having a well-earned rest, either catching up with a few hours' lost sleep, reading a book or going out to lunch with a friend. In the evening I would send John Two upstairs to my office to pay any outstanding bills and to return any difficult telephone calls. And he could have the rest of the evening off, unless I could sense a row coming on with my wife.

In which case he would be sent for. And if he lost the argument he would have to stay and watch *Friends* with her, and if he won he could nip out to the lav and I would come back in and settle down to watch something interesting.

'You're looking amazingly relaxed,' my wife said one weekend. 'The Prozac must be working.'

'I don't think it's got anything to do with the Prozac.'

'Oh, really? What is it then?'

'I'd put it down to sensible time management,' I said. 'You should try it sometime.'

I thought I had it cracked. I really did. An easy twenty-five-year run into retirement, at which point it would be all fun, fun, fun. But six months into my new arrangement everything started to go pear-shaped when John Two announced that he needed to have a little chat.

'I'm not at all happy with the way things are panning out,' he said stroppily.

'Oh. Why's that? I thought things were going just great between us.'

'Well, they aren't. I'm completely stressed out having to deal with all your shit.'

'But that's what you get for being me.'

'Well, I don't want to be you any longer,' he whined.

'That's tough. Anyway, I've had to put up with being me for forty years. You've only had to put up with being me for six months. You young people these days have just got no stamina.'

'Sod that,' he said. 'I just want to have a go at doing some of the fun things.'

'There aren't any. Not if you're me. Because I never enjoy anything anyway. There are just some things that are slightly less depressing than others.'

'Don't bandy semantics with me,' he snarled. 'Listen carefully. I want to have a go at some of the slightly less depressing bits. OK?'

'Well, you can't.'

'Why not?'

'Because you only exist to deal with all the crap.'

'No I don't,' he retorted. 'I'm a person in my own right.'

'I'll tell you what,' I said, in my best conciliatory manner. 'If you carry on doing a good job for the rest of the year, I'll let you go off by yourself on holiday for two weeks.'

'All right then,' he replied, considerably appeased. 'That's a deal.'

I'm sure that John Two intended to keep to the bargain. For the next few weeks there was a noticeable spring in his step as he went about his menial tasks with a renewed enthusiasm. But it didn't last.

The shit started to hit the fan when I got a string of unpaid parking tickets through the post for offences committed while John Two was out doing the weekly shopping.

'What are all these?' I demanded.

'They look like parking tickets to me.'

This didn't bode well.

'I can see that. And how did you get them?'

'I couldn't be bothered to find a proper space.'

'Well, that's fucking irresponsible. And I suppose you think I'm going to pay?'

'You're going to have to,' said John Two smugly. 'They don't allow seven-month-old blokes to have their own bank accounts.'

'I know. But you can kiss goodbye to your holiday now.'

With that, John Two stormed off and I went to bed. At eleven o'clock the next morning I was awoken by the phone ringing.

'Hello,' I said sleepily. 'Who's that?'

'It's me, Emily, from the office. Where are you?'

'I'm at work, aren't I?' I replied without thinking.

'I'll let you sort that one out for yourself,' she said nastily.

'No, of course I'm not,' I laughed. 'I'm here.'

'Brilliant.'

People have no idea of the difficulties of having a clone. Particularly when the lazy little bastard doesn't turn up to work.

'Look, I'm really sorry. I'll be in as soon as poss.'

John Two eventually reappeared two days later, having been on a massive bender. He looked terrible: his hair was matted, he had vomit down his front and his breath stank. We had reached the end of the line. He was now far more of a liability than an asset and it was time to get rid of him. But just as I was about to give him the usual redundancy patter of 'Thank you so much for all the long and loyal service you've given me. You've got two minutes to get out the building and any complaints should be addressed to my solicitor', John Two chipped in.

'I'm shorry,' he slurred. 'I know I've let you down. I didn't mean to. I jusht couldn't help it. It's sho painful having to be you the whole time. You're shuch a shad git. 'Scuse my language. Pleashe, pleashe, pleashe take me away from all this.'

'But you know what that would mean?'

'I do. But it'sh worth it.'

We both walked slowly out into the night, got in the car and headed north up the M6 towards Scotland. John Two spent the night either passed out or whimpering gently, while I stared ahead and said nothing. Sometime after breakfast we reached our destination.

'So this is it then,' I said.

John Two looked up at his birthplace and marched inside, while I followed along behind. He headed straight for the surgery.

'It'sh time to go,' he said. 'I'll missh you, John One.'

'I'll miss you too, John Two.'

Without further ado, John Two rolled up his sleeve and the doctor injected him with a lethal dose of barbiturates. And as he slumped back on the bed and gasped his last breath, a flurry of tears dripped from my eyes. It was almost as if I was watching part of me die.

Still, you can't be too sentimental about such things. He was only a clone, after all. And he had given me a whole load of hassle. So by the time I reached Birmingham the front passenger seat wasn't looking nearly so empty and reproachful. In fact, I was feeling remarkably chipper. Because I realized that my fundamental premise had been correct. Having a stand-in did work. My mistake had been choosing John Two. We had had a personality clash. Some might have said we were too similar, but I think that's stretching it. It was simply that he was too moody, too sensitive and too neurotic for my liking. And there was only room for one prima donna in my life. What I needed was someone a little more sensible and down-to-earth.

Which is how I came to find myself in the shabby first-floor offices of Monty's Double, just off the Mile End Road.

'And what can I do for you?' said the man there who introduced himself as Jim.

'I'm after a look-alike.'

'Well,' he said. 'I've got a few Princess Dis available. There's not been much call for them lately. But if you're looking for something cheap and cheerful, I can do you a good price on a Fergie. I can hardly give them away these days.'

'Er. Thanks,' I said. 'I was actually looking for someone who looked like me.'

'Oh,' he replied. 'Should I know who you are?'

'No.'

'You see, we only really do look-alikes of famous people.'

'But I thought you might have a central register of faces, because these days so many unknowns become instant celebs that you must worry you will get caught on the hop.'

'That's not the way the business works, sir.'

'Well, could you keep your eyes open anyway? Just in case you come across someone you think might do.'

'I'll see what I can do.'

And Jim was as good as his word, for a few weeks later I got a letter from a bloke requesting a meet at the bandstand in Battersea Park. I got there a few minutes late and was just catching my breath when I heard:

'Pssst. Are you John?'

I spun round, and there he was. A little greyer than me, but nothing that couldn't be fixed, and in all other respects a dead ringer for yours truly.

'Yeah. Who are you?' I asked.

'I don't give out my name.'

'Well, do you mind if I call you John Three?'

'Why John Three?'

'It's a long story.'

'OK. Sure. If that's what you want. Now, what is it you are after exactly?'

'It's a wee bit complicated.'

'Try me.'

So I bent his ear for the next twenty minutes. And by

the time I had finished, John Three was grinning broadly.

'You know what, John One?' he said. 'You don't mind if I call you John One, do you?'

'Be my guest,' I replied calmly. 'Everyone else does.'

'Well, I reckon we might just be in business. You see, the reason I decided to offer myself as a look-alike was because I was fed up with my life, too. Only my problem is the exact opposite of yours. My life is so fucking perfect that it's almost unreal. It's like I'm living in a fairy tale. My wife thinks the sun shines out of my arse. She's always pleased to see me, she always wants to watch what I want to watch on the TV. She's just too good to be true. And I've got the same kind of thing going on at work. I'm tremendously popular and everyone thinks I'm absolutely indispensable to the company. I've even tried screwing a project up on purpose, but the client thought I was being outlandishly innovative and gave us a whole load of new business. And to cap it all, I've never had a day's illness in my life. But you will be a real challenge for me. Being a fuck-up and getting grief from everyone for it will help me make sense of my life.'

'I'm glad to hear it,' I said drily.

'Mind you,' he continued, 'I'll only be you on a part-time basis. Two or three hours a day would be all I could manage. Any more and I might end up a psychiatric case. No disrespect intended.'

Of course not.

'None taken. I know what you mean. I'll pay you extra for any overtime, though.'

'No chance.'

With that we shook hands and agreed the deal. And very nicely it's worked out, too. Whenever I'm finding myself too much or John Three isn't finding himself enough, we give each other a ring and swap identities. I nip off to Bromley – that's where he lives, though I can't give you the exact address for security reasons – and get pampered and found generally interesting and entertaining. And he comes over here for a panic attack and a row. Though I do wonder if he isn't slacking a bit, as my wife has been saying how conciliatory and easy-going I'm becoming in my old age.

But then maybe I really am becoming easy-going. And if I am, it's all down to John Three. Or stressbuster as I sometimes call him when we meet up for our ten minute debrief at the change-over. You see, John Three will kill me for saying this, but he really is one of the nicest blokes I've ever met. I won't hear a word against him. He's revolutionized my life, by giving me a little oasis of calm. I'd even consider introducing him to you lot one day – if I didn't know for certain that you had already met him.

FIFTEEN

. . . And to my godchildren I leave . . . absolutely nothing. Not because I'm terribly mean, but because I haven't got any. I've always been a bit put out about this. Very put out, to be frank. I haven't even made anyone's short-list. Which is plain insulting really. Everyone else I know seems to have dozens of the little bastards. Even my wife, that pillar of atheism and low moral standards, has a couple. What's more, she's even signed the adoption papers for two friends. So the social services haven't been as thorough as they might. But as for *moi?* Nothing, *nada*, zilch. It's as if I've been branded a paedophile. Well, I want to get the record straight. I am not a paedophile. I don't even like other people's children, let alone fancy them.

Enough of that, though. Now, where was I? Ah yes.

My will. Don't worry, I haven't had a major relapse into my morbid ruminations. Quite the reverse. Life is chugging along OK, thanks to John Three and that quiet word my dad had with me. I think I can cope with getting old now. Well, certainly a bit better. There's just one last bit of the jigsaw to slot into place and I reckon I'll be sorted. And that last piece is my will.

There are a number of popular myths about wills. One is that you will die the moment you make one. Some people do, some don't. What more can I say? Another is that they should be as clear and simple as possible. My parents subscribe to this one. They have spent a fortune in legal fees ensuring that their legacies can be executed with the minimum of hassle. Which is totally self-defeating. And I'm not talking in a financial sense, though they should have borne that in mind.

A will is not about the seamless transfer of goods and chattels from the deceased to designated beneficiaries. Nor is it about tax avoidance, though that can be part of it. A will is about making sure that part of you remains immortal, so that long after you've died you continue to exercise power and influence and generally annoy everyone still living. A will is an exercise in negativity; more of a won't than a will. In this context a straightforward will is perfectly ridiculous. Because if all the hungry vultures have to do is gather at the solicitor's office on the day after your funeral, listen to him witter for a few minutes and then collect a cheque, you'll be forgotten in seconds as your heirs go off on a massive squandering spree. And if you think I'm being unduly cynical, just take a walk round any cemetery you like and see how many long-neglected graves you find. Conclusive proof of the sheer pointlessness of writing a will that can't be contested.

I'm not planning to rob my family of their inheritance, such as it might be, though I do think that John Three will deserve a small cut. I just want them to have to work very hard for it. A drip-feed is what's required. With strings attached, of course. Each year Jo and Tom can collect a few hundred quid more, provided they've mounted an all-night vigil praying for my immortal soul, take out an 'In memoriam' notice in all the national papers and wear black throughout St John's week, as the period of mourning shall be known. I won't insist on my annual thanksgiving service being televised, but the very least I will settle for is a decent bash in a cathedral, attended by numerous pop stars, media celebs, fashion designers and Anthea Turner. Actually, I'm sorry, Anthea. Ever since you and Peter. . .

You've no idea how difficult it is to make a complicated will. Unless you're a solicitor, in which case you've had years of practice. Because you can put in all these codicils, but it's really hard to make sure that every little detail is followed to the letter. I know what my kids are like. They're like me. They'll mean well to begin with, but within a few years they'll be cutting every corner they can find. The all-night vigil will be down to a hasty genuflection, and the service will be a quick rendition of 'Candle in the Wind' on the car stereo.

None of which is good enough. There's no way I am going to be turned into some third-rate cowboy operation. My death has got to be milked ruthlessly and efficiently for every prayer and every penny. Which means that I've had to do far more than my fair share of the planning.

'What the fuck do you think you're doing?' yelled my wife, as she got off her motor bike.

'I'm gardening,' I replied.

'You've fucking chopped down my favourite magnolia tree,' she roared, giving no sign of having heard me.

'I didn't think the front garden was getting enough light.'

'So you unilaterally decided to get rid of it?'

Is there any other way of reaching a mature decision?

'I wanted to redesign things a bit.'

'Why?'

Tricky. But I had to tell her.

'I'm preparing my last resting-place.'

'What are you on about?'

'I'm creating a Temple of John. I've wasted the tree because I'm planning to flood the front garden and make a little island that will be strewn with flowers all year round.'

'You're deranged.'

'I'm not. It'll be terribly tasteful. And imagine what a great photo opportunity it will be for you. "Grieving widow alone with her thoughts on an island of love".'

'I wouldn't count on the grieving bit.'

But I could see she was hooked. She loved the idea of making it into *Hello!* and thereafter she threw herself wholeheartedly into the project. She helped construct a little ticket office by the front gate, tastefully laid out a few of my school reports and an old stamp collection in the John Heritage Museum, aka the living-room, designed a few donkey rides for the theme park, John's World of Adventures, and bulldozed several adjoining houses to create enough parking spaces.

And I've got to say the whole thing looked extremely impressive by the time it was ready.

'How much do you think we could charge?' she asked, admiring her handiwork.

'Fifteen pounds a ticket, I should think.'

'The rides and cream teas will be extra, won't they?'

'Of course,' I said. 'But £15 to meditate by my graveside is still fantastically good value.'

'You don't think we're underpricing ourselves, do you?' she queried. 'After all, you'll be dead, so the money won't matter much to you one way or the other.'

'No. It's best to start low to get the punters in. Besides, there'll be loads of hidden extras.'

'Like what?'

'There'll be tons of flowers and teddy bears to flog back to Interflora and Hamley's, for a start.'

'That's true. We might even get an environmental award for recycling.'

'Over my dead body.'

'That goes without saying.'

Naturally, the goings on *chez* Crace attracted a considerable amount of attention worldwide. Begging letter after begging letter arrived from large multinational companies asking to use my signature in their advertising and marketing campaigns. Banks wanted to name PEPs after me, Tony Blair changed his name to John and made a personal appeal to the nation about how distraught he was at losing his hair and M&S became J&S, in recognition of my trendsetting elegance.

There were a few hassles to put up with, though. Like Jeffrey Archer's endless invites. Like having my life turned into a film for cable TV. But these were more than compensated for by one phone call in particular.

'Hi. Can I speak to John Crace?'

'Speaking.'

That's one thing people love about me. My availability. Most folk only have to get a whiff of celebdom and they're screening their calls behind secretaries and PRs to create an illusion of importance. But that isn't my style. Perhaps I'm too nice to be a celeb. Ah well, too late to worry about that now.

'It's Cliff's agent, here.'

'Hi, Cliff's agent.'

'Cliff was wondering whether you were going to have a concert after you died, and whether you would like him to perform.'

'I wasn't thinking of having a concert, actually. I was thinking of having an annual concert on the third Saturday of every July on Tooting Bec Common.'

'What a great venue. Cliff loves the acoustics. Look, if you want, I can do you a block booking. I can guarantee he will appear for the first 100 concerts.'

'Christ. Won't he be a bit old?' I said. 'Even if I died tomorrow he'd be nearly 160 by the time his contract was up.'

'Don't be ridiculous. Cliff doesn't get old. He is forever young.'

'Yeah, I'm sorry. I've had a lot of things on my mind. It sounds good to me. As long as he promises to always do "Congratulations" as an encore.'

'Done.'

What a legacy to the nation that will be. A celebration of Middle of the Roadness. Cliff and John. It has a bit of a ring to it. Shame I won't be there to see it, really.

Behind every public figure there is an intensely private, sensitive soul lurking. And I am no exception. So while I had to spend a lot of time making sure that the riff-raff – many of whom feel as if they know me personally – would be catered for on my death, I would also like to say that I made a number of more intimate decisions at home, in the bosom of my family, away from the glare of publicity.

The first was that it would be OK to write about my death in a string of clichés. It's the done thing. *Noblesse oblige*.

The second concerned organ transplantation. Living on in someone else had its attractions. Obviously I wouldn't have fancied being transferred into someone poor or ugly, but I think you're allowed to nominate your categories of recipients. But what I worried about was how the people I gave my bits to would cope with the responsibility. It's not easy having eyes like mine. Women go wild for them, and if they were given to someone who wasn't used to that sort of thing, would they be able to cope?

And what would it be like to be in another person's body? Would I become gay if I was put in another bloke? Or would I just be rejected? And would it feel quite horny wandering around inside a woman all day?

My body was certainly up for a change. From the moment I first picked up a donor card, all my organs started playing up. My heart palpitated, I got kidney stones and my eyes blurred.

'What's going on with me?' I asked Vicky, one of my wife's deeper friends.

'Just listen to your body,' she soothed. 'It will tell you what you need to know.'

And it did. I was lying in the garden, drinking in the silence of contemplation, when a little voice said to me:

'Oi, John.'

'What?'

'Don't be alarmed, but it's me, your heart, talking to you.'

'What do you want?'

'I've been asked to have a word with you by all your major organs.'

'OK. Go ahead,' I said.

'Well, we'd all like to move on.'

'Why?'

'Because we're all bored stiff. Your liver's had nothing challenging to do since you gave up alcohol. Ditto the kidneys. And the only thing that really stretches me and your lungs is the odd day of high pollution. And your eyes haven't seen anything hallucinatory or vaguely interesting for fucking ages.'

'But I thought that was the kind of life you like to lead.'

'That's what doctors say, but they don't understand how we organs feel deep down,' said my heart lyrically. 'We need something to test us a bit. You remember Paul? Well, his heart was a good mate of mine. And I was always dead envious, because he had so much to do. Put him in a room full of other hearts and he would be the life and soul, God rest him. Other hearts just ignore me, because I'm so dull. Just your regulation seventy-two beats a minute apart from when you go for a run. I'd like to go crazy sometimes – down to forty, then up to 120. Like I used to do in the old days.'

'I tell you what,' I said. 'If you promise not to give out on me in the next twenty-five years, I promise to be more interesting when I retire.'

'Do we have to wait that long?'

''Fraid so. It'll take at least that long to complete my funeral arrangements.'

'All right then.'

'And you're certain you have permission to make that decision on behalf of all the other organs?'

'Yup.'

So there I had it. The deal which I had been wanting all along. A cross-my-heart promise that I wasn't going to die until I was at least sixty-five; and surely my body wasn't going to pack in the moment the going got fun. Middle age was going to be survivable. Not just mentally but physically too. Which was good. Otherwise I think I might have gone mad.

SIXTEEN

'What's God, Daddy?' said Jo.

'It's hard to explain.'

'Georgia says he's everywhere. How can God be everywhere?'

'Umm, it's something you sort of believe or you don't.'

'And do you believe it, Daddy?'

To tell you the truth, I didn't know what I believed, really. Which is why I haven't mentioned God up till now. I didn't see how anyone could say anything firm one way or the other. He might exist. Or he might not. On balance, I'd rather he did. End of story. But being the Paddy Ashdown of theological debate had often opened me up to accusations of spiritual bankruptcy. As if.

It's true I'd never been the most questioning of blokes

when it came to religion. I'd never bothered to nip down to Stonehenge for the summer solstice. I'd never became a Buddhist, devoting myself to a lifetime's chanting and meditation. I'd never converted to Catholicism and crawled on my hands and knees to Santiago de Compostela. I'd never nailed myself to a crucifix in the Philippines. I'd never denounced Salman Rushdie. Other than for incomprehensibility. And I'd certainly never been born again. Neither had I become an atheistic rationalist – but then you wouldn't expect that from someone who's been certified.

No. All I'd done was trot off to church in an aimless sort of way twice a year and offered up a prayer or two in hope when I was in the shit. Which had come to a lot of prayers over the years. But nothing hard-core. Nothing really committed. Because it hadn't been necessary.

You see, being the son of a vicar conferred certain privileges. Like the guarantee of an afterlife – if there is one. This may come as a surprise to you, but religion is no different from any other business. Nepotism rules. God knows that he can't offer vicars huge salaries, rail discounts or their own TV station, so he offers family deals to the afterlife instead. So it's tough shit whether you think I deserve it or not. If it's there, I'm in. My place is booked. You'll just have to wait and see.

However, my lack of firm religious belief wasn't inspired by smugness and complacency – both of which would have been perfectly understandable given the circumstances. No. I was the way I was because my dad had told me that God didn't like toadies. Apparently he can't stand people who try to buy their way into heaven with endless shows of good works, parades of piety and out-bursts of mass fervour. God doesn't need any of that. His ego isn't that big. He wants a bit of respect – the odd acknowledgement that he's boss from time to time – and that's it. He wants people in heaven that he can have fun with. His view is that we're all going to be there for long enough, so we might as well enjoy it. Who wants to hang out with a bunch of Bible-bashers for all eternity? Certainly not God.

So I reckoned it was just as important to look on death as a social as much as a spiritual event. Which is why I was not going to make the mistake of being buried in a suit. If you're going to have to wear something for ever and ever, it should at least be something you feel comfort-able in. Now, I know that's it's only natural that you want to make a good impression when you first arrive in heaven, but there are going to be a number of Crusaders up there who've been wandering around in chain mail for eight hundred years who rather wished they'd opted for something less formal.

But we're not just talking comfort. We're also talking style. Because heaven must be celeb city. What's more, its rules decree there can be no minders or PR people to keep us proles at bay. So anyone you want to talk to you can. Princess Di, Marilyn Monroe, James Dean, Frank Sinatra — they're all up there. You may have to queue, though, as these are currently the top four attractions. There must be at least a four-year queue for Di at the moment, but what's a few years when you've got all the time in the world? Personally, I will be giving her queue a miss, as she must still be furious with me for not having an affair with her. But that's just our problem. Don't let me influence you in any way.

You've got to plan your visits with care. It can look a bit desperate to join the all-male queue for Marilyn, and you certainly wouldn't want to be seen dead – not that you'd have a choice – among all the spaced-out hippies lining up for Timothy Leary and Allen Ginsberg. There's no guarantee that any of these celebs will be pleased to see you, though. They're obliged to be polite, but no more. So you'll get your full five minutes, but don't for a second imagine that you're automatically going to become bosom buddies. You may be dead, but it doesn't make you any more interesting.

Heaven must an awfully crowded place and I guessed I was going to feel a bit lost to start with. So I planned to make my big entrée with a tour of the relatives. But I couldn't just assume that all my dead relatives would be pleased to see me. I mean, why should they break the habits of a lifetime just because they're in heaven? People's characters can't change that quickly; you can't be an out-and-out bastard while you're alive and expect to metamorphose into a harp-playing angel when you stop breathing.

In any case, my dad says that while celebs have a duty to be friendly in heaven as a punishment for being so self-important on earth, ordinary people are expected to be much more honest up there than they are down here. So you are almost certainly going to find that a number of people who said they liked you while they were alive, have actually always hated your guts. And they won't hesitate to let you know it. They'll cut you. Dead.

Which is why it was important to have things out with as many of my relatives as I could while we were all still breathing.

'Hi, Mum.'

'Hi, John,' she sniffed, wiping away a few traces of white powder from her nose.

'Can I have a word?'

'Yeah, if you're quick,' she said, glancing at her watch. 'We're off on holiday again in twenty minutes.'

'Where to this time?'

'Trekking in the Himalayas.'

'I wish I was old enough to do that,' I said wistfully.

'Well, you're not and that's that. You'll have to make do with your dreary trips to Devon.'

'Don't panic. I wasn't thinking of going with you.'

'Good. So what do you want, then?'

'I was wondering if you would mind if I came and visited you when I was dead.'

'What are you talking about?'

Hadn't she heard of the afterlife?

'I won't treat your place as a hotel.'

'Are you feeling OK?'

Obviously not. Or maybe she wasn't comfortable talking about her own demise. But I persisted.

'Up in heaven. Can I . . . ?'

'I heard you the first time. But what makes you so certain you won't snuff it first?'

'I've done a deal with my heart.'

'Have you taken your medication?'

Which was where the conversation ended. So I still wasn't sure where I stood *vis à vis* my parents, though I was fairly confident that they would allow me the odd visit. But I was confused. Had I just embarrassed my mum by breaking some protocol that forbids making arrangements for the hereafter, or was she being evasive because she didn't want to make an appointment that she knew she wouldn't be able to keep? In other words, maybe there was no afterlife. It had just been some kind of mental construction that my dad had invented to keep me happy. To make me think that there might be something to look forward to one day.

Emptiness and nothingness seemed such a waste. I mean, why bother to go through all the effort of living, of caring about other people, of creating clones, of becoming famous, of going mad, if there was no reward at the end of it? Other than to see your relatives desecrating your memory. What would happen to all my psychic lethargy? Would it be dissipated in localized drizzle over SW16? Or would it not even manage that?

Once again, it was my dad who came to the rescue.

'You seem a bit down,' he said.

'You could put it like that. Or you could call it terminal.'

'Oh dear. Can I help?'

'I don't think that drugs are the solution.'

'I wasn't going to offer you any. Now what's going on?' he asked.

We talked at length. About certainty. About uncertainty. About faith, really.

'There's someone I'd like you to talk to,' he said, as we came to the end of the conversation.

'Who?'

'Never you mind.'

And with that he bound my hands and feet, blindfolded me and bundled me into the back of his car. An hour and a half later we came to a halt at what sounded like the end of a long gravel drive. I heard my dad whisper to someone, and then the boot opened and I was carried off. When the ropes were untied and my blindfold removed, I found myself lying on the floor of a darkened, unfurnished room.

My dad looked down on me kindly.

'I'm sorry for all this hush-hush, top-secret stuff,' he explained. 'But the person I want you to speak to rather insists on it.'

'Who is it?'

'Can't you guess?'

'Prince Charles? He's hot on spirituality.'

'No, you berk, it's God.'

'I don't believe you.'

'Well, you'd better start,' he said. 'Hence the need for privacy. Because God is generally expected to be everywhere at once, and if people had any idea he was here with you, all hell would break loose. We'd have millions of gatecrashers, and every dictator in every corner of the earth would try to bump off a few more million innocent people when he wasn't looking. Anyway, God's a very busy person. So don't let me down by making an idiot of yourself.'

And with that he skipped out of the room.

'Hello, John,' a disembodied voice boomed.

'Who's that?'

'It's God.'

'Oh, come on, Dad. Stop pissing about with the special effects,' I said.

'This is not a good start,' the voice replied. 'I am God. For my sake, can't you take anything on trust? Now stop wasting my time. I'm extremely tied up with all the world's hot spots, and I don't normally make personal calls. But your dad is a good bloke, so I'm seeing you as a favour to him.'

'I didn't think it would be on my account,' I replied, hurt.

'Well, what do you expect? You're such hard work. You've been a trial to your family. You've been a trial to your friends. And to be honest, you've been a trial to me, too. Though not as much as someone like Pol Pot, of course.'

'And how is the old mass murderer?'

'None of your business. It's you I'm concerned with right now.'

'OK, then, God. Maybe you can help me. Is there an afterlife?'

'I'm not telling you.'

'Why not?'

'It's a surprise.'

'I don't like surprises.'

'Now there's a surprise.'

'I didn't think God was meant to be sarcastic.'

'Well, there's another surprise for you,' he said, chuckling to himself.

'Please,' I pleaded. 'Tell me about the afterlife.'

'No.'

'Why not?'

'Because it wouldn't make any difference.'

'It would. I would feel reassured.'

'Maybe. But your life would be exactly the same.'

'How do you mean?'

'Well,' he explained, 'I've noticed that shitty people are still shitty people regardless of whether they believe in me, and nice people are still nice people regardless of whether they believe in me.'

'And what about neurotics like me?' I asked.

'You're fucked. You're so busy worrying about the future that the present escapes you entirely.'

'But do I have a future?'

'I'm not going to tell you.'

'Is it possible for me to become less neurotic?'

'How should I know? I'm only your God, not your sodding shrink. Look, I must go now. Wars to stop, famines to end, you know how it is.'

'Sure.'

'One last thing, though,' he said with a snigger. 'You shouldn't always listen to your heart.'

'What?' I replied, panic-struck.

'Lighten up a bit. I was only joking.'

Oh were you? Were you really?

Also available in Vista paperback

Baby Alarm

Thoughts From a Neurotic Father

JOHN CRACE

'Made me laugh so hard I split my episiotomy stitches' Kathy Lette

When a man reaches a certain age he knows he's never going to be asked to partner Cantona up front. That can be pretty scary. Children provide a way out – you get your own baby to love who will think you are the funniest, handsomest man alive – and they offer the chance of immortality, too!

What you can't foresee are the drawbacks – a never-ending cycle of anxiety and getting it right, whether you're physically capable of becoming a father, whether the baby will be O.K . . . and that's before your wife tells you she's pregnant.

ISBN 0 575 60268 6

VISTA